FAST FOOD FACTS

Here it all is
This book gives the facts that the companies keep to themselves. Here are the missing labels and the nutrititional details. Here, too, are the facts about working in the fast food industry and the new global empires being built by the fast food multinationals.

FAST FOOD FACTS

A COMPENDIUM OF THE HIDDEN SECRETS OF FAST FOOD CATERING

TIM LOBSTEIN, PH D,

Assisted by Fiona Carruthers, Michelle Rae Kirwin and Morag Haynes

The London Food Commission

Camden Press Ltd, London

Published in 1988 by
Camden Press Ltd
43 Camden Passage, London
N1 8EB, England

Typeset by
Photosetting & Secretarial
Services, Yeovil
and printed and bound by
A. Wheaton & Co. Limited,
Exeter, Devon

Designed by Tony Garrett

British Library CIP Data

Lobstein, Tim
The fast food guide.
1. Convenience food.
Nutritional values
1. Title
641.1

ISBN 0 948491-48-5

Cover illustration by
John Davey

Preface

We eat over 20 million fast food meals each *week* in Britain. Yet few of us have any idea of what is in that food. Unlike supermarket shelves, fast food caterers display no labels telling us what is in these meals – no labels on take-away foods, no labels on self-service foods, no labels on hot snack foods.

- Are chips fattening?
- Is a burger and shake nutritious?
- Which additives do they contain?

This guide to the hidden world behind the fast food counter shows you exactly what you are getting when you order your take-away meal. It lists the nutrients and additives in a broad range of familiar fast foods. The book also shows you what you are *not* getting – the missing nutrients you need to survive the fast food experience. And it gives details of the unexpected meat, fish and insect products to be found in fast foods and where you might find allergy-inducing ingredients that you didn't expect.

The only book of its kind, it gives the details you will otherwise never get to see. Dr Tim Lobstein, project officer at London Food Commission, has spent two years compiling the information from trade sources and from a special analysis undertaken by Southwark Public Protection. This book gives you first chance to discover *what is in fast food for you?*

Acknowledgements

This book is dedicated to the patience and tolerance shown by my partner Kathy Adams.

As principal author of this book, I am pleased to use this page to say *thank you* to the many people who have contributed to its creation. In particular, I am indebted to three students on placements from their courses who found themselves caught up in the collection of information for this book: Fiona Carruthers, Morag Haynes and Shelly Kirwin. They claim that they enjoyed the experience and I shall try to believe that they did.

My colleagues, the staff at the London Food Commission, have been more than generous in their time and efforts supporting this book as it underwent numerous revisions. In particular Issy Cole-Hamilton and Tim Lang have spent long hours peering at photocopied typescripts and making many suggestions.

More useful comments and criticisms have also come from other individuals who read early drafts and I am indebted for their support and interest. Of especial help, acting in their own capacity, have been:

Ian Bellerby (then Chief Trading Standards Officer, Haringey), Ben Birnberg (B M Birnberg and Co, London), Professor Michael Crawford (Zoological Society, London), Yiannis Gabriel (Lecturer in Business Administration, Thames Polytechnic), Michael Jacobson (Director, Centre for Science in the Public Interest, Washington DC), Rekha Patel (then Community Dietitian, Islington), Philip Pearson (Hotel and Catering Officer, Transport and General Workers Union), Diane Plamping (Senior Lecturer in Community Dentistry, University College London), Professor Aubrey Sheiham (Department of Community Dental Health, University College London), Bob Stevens (Public Analyst, Southwark), Lynn Stockley (Health Education Authority), and Ann Tobin (researcher and ex-fast food employee).

Tim Lobstein

Your quick guide to the fast food facts

"There is no doubt that the fast food industry provides a whole range of ready-to-serve foods whose importance to the British diet is seldom appreciated. The Ministry of Agriculture Fisheries and Food has found that by and large the products of the fast food industry compare well with other food products and represent valuable sources of protein, vitamins and minerals to customers who might otherwise forgo them.

" I know that some fast food retailers are already providing their customers with useful information to help choose a satisfactory diet and I would encourage this practice."

Peggy Fenner, 1986, then Parliamentary Secretary, Ministry of Agriculture Fisheries and Food (reference 0.1).

Are fast foods fattening?

It can take over half an hour of swimming to burn the calories from just one portion of chips. A single fast food meal could provide you with well over half your daily calorie needs but still leave you hungry just a few hours later. For a look at the calories in fast foods –

See Chapters 3 and 5, and Appendix 1

Fast Food: Good or bad for your health?

Chips have vitamin C in them and milk shakes have calcium. But some fast food outlets put sugar on the chips or even in hot dogs and meat pies. Some fast food meals have over twenty teaspoons of pure fat in them. And some have more than half your recommended daily salt intake even before you add any salt yourself. To compare fast foods for fat and salt, vitamins and minerals –

See Chapters 3 and 4, and Appendix 1

Are fast foods a problem for people with special food needs?

Watch out, vegetarians, there may be beef fat in your french fries or even in your apple pie. Pork-avoiders, there may be pig fat in your beefburger. Food allergy sufferers, there may be azo dyes in your fish batter, gluten in your soft fruit whip or milk in your chicken pie. Check the ingredients –

See Chapter 2 and Appendix 2

Can I get a balanced meal from a fast food outlet?

Many fast food meals are short on essential minerals and vitamins. We looked at a selection of meals offered by fast food restaurants and worked out what was there and what was missing. To make sure you get a balance –

See Chapter 4 and Appendix 1

Your quick guide to the fast food facts

But the meat is good for you, isn't it?

Hot dogs can have as little as 25% lean meat. Sausage rolls may have less than 7% lean meat. And what the industry calls "lean meat" could put you off meat for life. To get an idea of what meat you are being sold –

See Chapter 2

"A SLUM INDUSTRY... that would earn a place in any modern version of Dante's 'Inferno'."

Robin Murray, former Chief Economic Advisor, Greater London Council, describing the fast food industry (reference 0.3).

Do fast foods have additives?

Without the ingredient labels that you get on food packets in the shops, you can't tell what might be added to your fast food meal. Among others, we found colourings in fish and chips and in pilau rice, preservatives in salad dressings and saccharin in the gherkins. To check out the additives –

See Chapter 2 and Appendix 2

Compare the products

Companies like to tell you the good news, not the bad news. For a look at what they say, and the information to help you make a choice –

See Chapter 6 and Appendix 1

Is working in fast food restaurants fun? Could you save to buy a house?

Catering is one of the lowest-paid areas of work. Wages and conditions are not attractive yet large numbers of people work for the big fast food companies at some time in their life. For what workers have to say –

See Chapter 9

You and the fast food business

Fast food consumption is growing in Britain and around the world. New products are being developed and marketed, new ways of catching customers are being dreamt up. To get the sort of deal you want, to make complaints and to get your voice heard –

See Chapter 10 and Appendix 3

Contents

Tables

Chapter 1 **Getting the facts**

"Consumers need both information and education if they are to reap the full benefits of the market place. They need the information, the facts about goods and services: they need to be educated so they can analyse those facts before making a purchase."

US Presidential Proclamation by Ronald Reagan, 1985 (reference 0.2).

Fast food is big business. When Kentucky Fried Chicken opened their Marble Arch restaurant in London in late 1987, they found they were getting a massive 3,500 customers *every day*[1/1]. McDonald's estimated they would get around *a million and a half customers in a year* when they proposed opening a store in Hampstead, London[1/2].

That is a lot of fried chicken and a lot of burgers. And a lot of wrappers and cartons. And a lot of cash, too, with the big three – Wimpy, McDonald's and Kentucky – selling £500,000,000-worth of their products in the UK in 1987. But, as we show in this book it is also a lot of fat and a lot of calories.

This book shows that, although fast food stores and take-away restaurants provide a useful and in many ways desirable service, they are not providing the quality of food that your body might want, nor the sort of information you need to make better choices about your diet and health.

Fast food is great for a quick and convenient meal at fairly low cost and little effort. But you have the right to expect that the food on offer is of a good quality and can help you get a balanced diet, that it is not adulterated and that it is clearly labelled. This book provides the information you need to judge the food you are buying.

"Junk?"

A survey of 19 to 21 year-olds asked what foods they liked to eat but knew they should not eat. Chips came top of the list, confectionery came next, with cakes and buns, fried fatty foods and meat products following close behind.[1/3] In a school-children's survey in North London, chips, hamburgers, hot dogs, sausages and fizzy drinks were among the foods most often thought to be "unhealthy".[1/4] A third survey put hamburgers at the top of a list of housewives' perceptions of "least healthy foods".[1/5]

It is clear that those who eat fast food are suspicious of its nutritional value. A London Food Commission survey found that barely 20% of fast food eaters rated the food they were eating as being good for their health. (And when asked "Would you believe a fast food manufacturer who said the food was good for you?" over 83% said they would not!)

Can fast food eaters have a balanced diet? Consumers are presented with an array of foods in fast food restaurants, with some items more likely to contribute to poor health and some less likely. A dietitian would say that no single food will cause ill-health; that it is the balance of the food in the overall diet that matters. Too much fat in one meal, for example, can be balanced by lower-fat meals at other times.

But the same dietitians will add that many people are eating too much food loaded with sugar and fat, high in calories but low in nutrients. To balance such food means finding other foods that are high in the missing nutrients but low in calories. So the question is: "Do fast food meals provide an opportunity for finding nutrient-rich foods, and so making a balanced meal?" This book shows that the answer is: "It might be possible, but it isn't very easy."

If you wanted a take-away meal to be low in fat you might not know which food to choose. If you wanted to avoid sugar you might not know which dish had added sugar and which didn't. Without information you cannot make an informed choice. This doesn't only apply to the cooking it also applies to the quality of the ingredients used. Who, at home, would leave out the egg in a batter and put in yellow colouring chemicals instead?

The food needs proper labelling. You need to see which foods are high-fat and which are low. You need to see which foods are additive laden and which are additive-free. Even if you do not read the labels, the very fact that the information is displayed can serve to shame the companies into improving their product ranges.

If fast food customers don't have clear information on the nutrients and the ingredients in their food – the bare minimum of what is needed – then they cannot be expected to make informed choices. Manufacturers and caterers have been keeping their secrets for too long and it has worked against their own best interests. Instead of giving facts they have encouraged secrecy. In such circumstances consumers become suspicious. It is perhaps not surprising that fast food has an image of being unhealthy and little more than "junk".

This book starts to remedy the situation. It discusses the current nutritional recommendations and advice, and gives the information you need to look at fast foods with a critical eye. It looks at the place of fast foods in a healthy diet and outlines the pros and cons of some sample meals.

This book also looks at the ingredients – the details that the customers are not shown. It uncovers some ingredients in fast foods that you might not have expected, and certainly wouldn't have chosen if you were cooking for yourself.

By looking at what is in fast food it is possible to see how the food industry thinks and how it likes to portray itself. This book looks at the images fast food companies project and the reality behind those images. It looks at the working conditions for those who take a job in fast food catering. And it looks at the growth in fast food chains, their concentration in the hands of a few large companies and what new developments might be sprung upon you in the next few years.

The book finishes with a guide for consumers wanting to take action. There is no need to stand by and suffer – you can start making changes from today to make sure you get the food you really want to eat. You are the customers, and you need to say clearly what you expect.

Finding the facts

To produce this book we wrote to the big fast food companies, we visited trade exhibitions, we researched the scientific and commercial journals, we gathered information from the USA, Europe, Asia and Australia. We read market reports and stockbrokers' analyses, and we talked to the fast food eaters on the street. We even went around the back of the fast food stores to check out the dustbins.

No one has collected all this information in one place before. It is a virtual encyclopaedia of information on fast foods. It covers the more popular types of fast food from the well-known chains of high street restaurants that offer a limited list of foods with quick service to the take-away foods which the smaller, independent restaurants sell. You will find details on the main foods sold in fish and chip shops, hamburger bars and fried chicken stores, as well as some information on foods sold in sandwich bars and pizzerias, and some dishes from Caribbean, Greek, Turkish, Indian and Chinese restaurants and cafes.

From the facts that we publish here, the reader will see that fast foods can have significant and serious effects on a customer's health. Over half of us can expect to become obese. Nearly half of us will die of diet-related heart disease, many before we retire. Many of us will develop diet-related cancer. Nearly all of us will have diet-related tooth decay. Our growing consumption of fast foods will have an increasing effect on our health. If we do not take a critical stand today we may well regret the results tomorrow.

History shows that when the public assert their right to know what is happening, to monitor and expose bad practices and to throw doubt on the information given by vested interests, then the public can exert maximum pressure for change. This pressure can work: the 18th century food standards legislation and the 19th century anti-adulteration laws bear witness to the public exposure of bad practices. As this book shows, the struggle must continue even in the last years of the 20th century.

We believe that fast food companies must take more responsibility to ensure that the food they provide is of a quality you can rely on, and they should give you the information you need to choose precisely what you want.

When this book quotes facts and figures there is no secret about where they came from. We put on each occasion a note like this[2/3] indicating the source of our material. The number refers to the list of references towards the end of this book.

Chapter 2 **The inside story**

Concern about poor quality food and food adulteration scandals in the last century, such as chalk-water in the milk, sand in the sugar and birch-leaves in the tea, led national government and local authorities to set regulations about the standards of food permitted to be sold. In recent years, however, there have been moves to replace these fixed standards in favour of "informative labelling". This means that as long as the label declares, say, only 15% meat in a can of chicken casserole, it can still be sold as "Chicken Casserole". You have to read the small print to find out if you are getting what you expect.

Changing the regulations away from agreed standards and towards declarations of content puts all the responsibility for finding good quality food onto the consumer. "It is up to the customer to choose what they want to buy" say the manufacturers. "They can always read the label. We don't force them to buy low-quality foods if they don't want to."

The argument is weak at the best of times, but it falls completely into ruins when it comes to buying fast food, because *no declaration of the content of fast food is required.* No legal regulation obliges fast food companies to tell customers the ingredients of the food they are serving up. There is only the general obligation not to be found telling lies to the customers.

We have asked several fast food companies for details about their products, and apart from a few honourable exceptions, we have not been given the details we asked for.

It is quite bizarre that customers should have no right to know how much meat is in their burger or saveloy. Nor whether the meat is lean or fatty. Nor whether it is made of muscle or intestines, or whether it comes entirely from cows or is mixed with other animals' meats. *There is no legal right to know.* There may be colouring in the fish batter, or sugar in the pizza or saccharin in the pickles, but you will probably never be told.

For many people it may not be a matter of importance,

but for some – as we shall discuss shortly – it can be essential to know these things. Yet the information is withheld. Until now, that is. This book begins to lift the lid off the fast food pot to reveal the facts manufacturers prefer to keep hidden.

Reconstructing food

The meat you are sold in a fast food shop may not be quite what you imagine it should be. You might assume, for example, that a chicken is a chicken, whether you buy it in the supermarket or in a take-away dish. But the chickens we buy from the deepfreeze or the butcher's window are the best of the bunch. There are large numbers of disfigured and bruised animals, and damaged and broken carcasses, which get sold off to the catering trade. They are processed into unrecognisable forms, coated in "special recipe" batters or crumbs and served up deep-fried in golden bite-sized pieces.

With fish from a fish and chip shop, the product is, usually, a single piece of fish deep frozen and thawed before being dipped in a concoction of white flour, calcium phosphate, sodium bicarbonate, with dyes developed for the textile industry: tartrazine and sunset yellow. The dyes make the batter look like egg-batter though there is no egg present at all. (Some manufacturers of the batter mixes are now replacing these dyes with other added colours – the so-called natural dyes like annatto – though there is no evidence that this is better for our health.)

But not all fish is whole. Various fish dishes might look like whole pieces but in fact consist of broken bits of fish (minced fish pieces) reformed and coated with crumb or batter. Fish fingers are a good example. And some 80% of breaded scampi is minced and re-formed pieces, much of it with more breading than scampi flesh.

But ask at the counter of any fast food store for a list of the ingredients of a dish like this, and the best answer you can hope for is a "Sorry. Not available."

What is lean meat?

Recent changes in food legislation now allow manufacturers of meat products to add far more fat and water than ever before and still say that their product is made of meat. Even a *100% beefburger* can have added water (as much as 15%) and added fat (up to 35%).

If something is called an *economy burger* it can be 40% non-meat, and even the parts that are meat can be at least one third pure fat. *A beef*burger need not be pure beef, but can have up to 20% other animals' meat (e.g. pig, chicken, tur-

Table 2.1 **Parts of animals which can be used as lean meat or offal**

"Lean meat" permitted in cooked and un-cooked products:
Mammals
Flesh, diaphragm, heart, skin, sinew, pancreas, thymus, kidney, rind, head muscle, tail, tongue, liver and gristle
Birds
Flesh, gizzard, liver, neck, gristle, sinew, skin and heart
Offal permitted in cooked products:
Mammals and birds
Brains, intestines, stomach, oesophagus, feet, spleen, spinal cord, udder, rectum, lungs and testicles
sources: 2'1

A quarterpound beefburger recipe might look like this:

Flake or grind
30 grams beef shin (including gristle, sinew and some fat)

Mix with
16 grams beef mince (including heart, tongue, and more fat)

Add
19 grams rusk and soyaflour
16 grams beef fat, pre-chopped

Blend with
20 grams water
2 grams salt and spices
1 gram monosodium glutamate and colouring
0.5 gram polyphosphates and preservative

Lastly stir in
10 grams MRM* (partly fat)

*MRM means mechanically recovered meat, obtained by stripping the remains of the carcass of every useful tissue, and grinding the bits into a fine slurry. (source 2'2)

key, or pork rind or lard). And an *economy beefburger* could legally be 40% pork fat.

A customer might assume that lean meat meant red muscle flesh, the sort you might buy in the butcher's for a Sunday roast, or at least the sort sold as stewing steak or mince. But to the food companies this is not what it means. Since the introduction of new meat regulations in 1986 in Britain, the makers of meat products can use parts of the animal listed in Table 2.1 and, especially in the case of fast foods, the customers would be none the wiser.

How do these components become a burger or hot dog? With a lot of help! Food technology has become quite sophisticated, with machines that can "tumble-massage" stripped carcasses to get the last shred of tissue off. There are fine chopping and grinding machines which can obliterate the lumps and stringy bits and blend this "meat" with an array of gluey additivies such as emulsifiers and thickeners. And there are forming machines which can reshape the resulting mix into hunks, chunks, fingers, wedges, steak-style, rib-style convincing foods.

Chemical make-weights

Meat used to make a meat product, like a sausage, a meat pie, or even a cooked cold joint, can, without breaking any law, be soaked in a solution of polyphosphate salts which have the effect of absorbing and holding water in the meat. A five pound shoulder of ham can, for just a few pence, become a six pound shoulder of ham. A four ounce "jumbo" beef sausage can consist of 1oz water, 1oz bread rusk, 1oz fat and 1oz "lean" meat. The water is held in place with the polyphosphates, as well as other emulsifiers and salts which help it cling to the fat and the meat. All this is then spiced up with some salt and pepper and a helping of monosodium glutamate, then sold in a bun for 80p.

Table 2.2 gives a list of declared meat content of some typical products used in fast foods and sandwich bars. But the declared meat content is not the whole story. Manu-

For a jumbo beef sausage you need

32 grams water
23 grams pork back fat and beef fat
20 grams beef head meat
18 grams rusk
10 grams turkey MRM*
5 grams emulsified rind
2 grams soya flour
1 gram milk protein
1 gram salt, spices
0.5 gram monosodium glutamate, colouring
0.5 gram polyphosphates and preservative

* For the note on MRM see the previous recipe. (source 2'2)

facturers can add at least 10% more water than they admit and as much as a third of the meat can be pure fat.

Soap and seaweed?

Emuslfiers, as their name suggests, emulsify or bind together fat and water. Soap and detergent are emulsifiers,

Table 2.2 **Some meat product ingredients**

Trade supplier & product	**Declared minimum meat** content (& minimum lean)	**Ingredients***
Westlers Hamburger	meat 80% ("lean" 52%)	Beef, other meat, starch, salt, wheatflour, soya, phosphate E450c, autolysed yeast, spices, preservative E250
Westlers Economy burger	meat 60% ("lean" 39%)	Meat, water, soya, flour, rusk, salt, onion powder, phosphate E450c, sugar, spice extracts, monosodium glutamate, meat flavour (HVP), preservative E223, garlic powder, vegetable oil, colours E150, E128, E102
Bristol Hot Dog sausage	meat 50% ("lean" 25%)	Pork, chicken, water, starch, salt, milk protein, soya, sugar, spices, phosphate E450c, antioxidant E301, preservative E250
Freshbake Saveloy sausage	meat 50% ("lean" 25%)	Pork, water, other meat, soya, starch, salt, spices, phosphate E450a, herbs, monosodium glutamate, preservative E223, flavouring, colour E128
Sun Valley Turkey Breast for sandwiches	meat 70% ("lean" 46%)	Turkey breast meat, water, salt, phosphates and emulsifiers E450a, 450b, E331, monosodium glutamate, sugar, milk, potato starch

* Ingredients change from time to time and company to company. These are examples of what some products contain. For more facts on the contents of fast foods, see ***Ingredients and Additives: The Details*** at the back of this book.

"E" numbers are the numbers which identify certain permitted additives (the "E" means they are permitted in EEC countries).

sources: company labels

Table 2.3 **Some foods thickened with wood, cotton, seaweed or tree resin extracts**

Item	*Thickener**
Potato Croquettes	E464
Chicken Pieces, southern-style	E466
Cheese and Onion Pastie	E466
Instant Noodles	E466
Milk shake mixes	E466, E407, 416
Soft-serve Ice cream	E407
French-style Dressing	E407
Horseradish Sauce	E465
Tomato Sauce	416
Mustard Sauce	E407

* Ingredients change from time to time and company to company. These are examples of some products we have found. For more facts on the contents of fast foods, see *Ingredients and Additives: The Details*, at the back of this book.

NB Thickener 416 has no "E" number as it has not been approved for use in all EEC countries.

source: company labels

and chemicals similar to soaps and detergents are used in large quantities in the food industry. To make a product which holds added water and added fat, and holds together in one piece, a manufacturer would use emulsifiers and similar thickening agents. These chemicals can even help to hold air in a product. Just whip up an emulsified mixture of fat and water with the appropriate colourings or flavourings, and you can create soft ice cream or mayonnaise or milk shake or even non-drip paint.

Another method used to bulk out products with low-cost ingredients is to use thickeners, gums, gelling agents and cellulose. These can increase the size and apparent value of a product. Traditionally gravies and sauces were thickened with flour or pastes like tomato paste. Nowadays manufacturers have available a large array of thickening and bulking agents ranging from low-nutrient modified starch, to seaweed extracts, tree resin and wood pulp.

E464 is a thickening agent, Hydroxypropyl Methyl Cellulose, derived from wood pulp or cotton. So is E465 Ethylmethyl Cellulose, while E466 Sodium Carboxymethyl Cellulose is made from cotton by-products. E407 Carageenan is made from seaweed and 416 Karaya Gum is the secretion of a tree native to India. Table 2.3 gives some examples of food products using these thickeners.

In our research we have found examples of foods similar to those listed in Table 2.3 but without the thickeners, indicating that such additives are not *necessary* in the food, but are added for other, perhaps commercial, reasons.

Old food for new

Preserving food so that it can be used long after it was harvested is not a new idea. We have had salted meat, smoked fish, dried fruit and pickled vegetables for many centuries. But none of these foods would pretend they were anything other than preserved food. Now, though, manufacturers have available a range of different chemicals that can prevent food from showing deterioration over long periods, without the consumer knowing.

Fresh-looking food that is in fact old and tired may well have lost some of its useful nutrients, but you might not recognise it. If food has no preservative and sits around for a long time, it will show obvious signs of its age. But if preserving agents are used then food can look fresh when in fact it is days, weeks or even months old. Baked pies, cooked meats and vegetables can all be kept fresh-looking and fresh-tasting, though they may have been stored for weeks.

Anti-oxidants are used to prevent fat from going rancid.

They can also serve to prevent colours, including added colours, from fading. Nitrite preservatives have replaced old-fashioned smoking methods for meats such as bacon. Anti-fungal agents stop mould from growing, which might reveal the true age of the product. As we shall indicate later in this chapter many of the chemical agents used are suspected of having undesirable effects on our health. But, especially with unlabelled fast foods, we have no way of knowing whether we are being sold genuinely fresh food or food that looks fresh but may be many months old.

Window dressing

One effect of adding cheap ingredients to a food product is that the result may not be particularly appealing. Lean meat filled out with fat, bread and water looks grey and tastes bland. It needs something extra. To make the magic difference, food "cosmetics" are used. Cosmetics can turn grey meat-paste to red or golden brown, can flavour plain milk with the delicate aroma of strawberries or bananas, and colour a milk shake a vibrant pink or yellow.

Food cosmetics have been around for a long time. Add salt, herbs and spices to a fatty dull dish and it is suddenly more tasty and attractive to the palate. But in recent years companies have developed over 3000 laboratory-produced chemicals available to colour and flavour the food you eat. The flavouring agents, whether made synthetically to mimic natural ones, or newly created in the laboratory, can now be pushed to their mouth-exploding limit with

Table 2.4 **Examples of groups of people with specific food requirements**

Group	*Estimated number*	*Avoid*
Muslims	1.3m	Some milk products, non-halal meats, pork, shellfish
Jews	0.3m	Meat and dairy together, eggs with blood, non-kosher meat, some fish and all shellfish, pork
Hindus	0.3m	Some egg and milk products, beef, some fish (many Hindus are totally vegetarian)
Sikhs	0.3m	Usually beef, some other meat and fish products (some Sikhs are vegetarian)
Vegetarians	1.3m	Products from dead animals
Vegans	0.01m	All animal products
Food intolerance sufferers	0.5m	Various foods, commonly milk, egg, flour or soya products
Food additive intolerance sufferers	0.03m	Range of additives, such as sulphites, benzoates, coal tar dyes, glutamates

flavour enhancers.

Colours finish off a product. Food can be coloured with chemicals derived from petrol or aluminium, or found in shellfish shells, burnt plants, flamingo feathers, buttercup flowers and even beetles' eggs! Added colours are there to sell the food to your eyes. Even the manufacturers and their representatives admit that there may be something deceptive going on here. "If we didn't add colours to our soft drinks people wouldn't buy them," admitted one industry spokesperson on television recently. "Customers would see that the drinks were just sugar and water, and wouldn't want them".

Dietary hazards

Food plays a major role in many cultures and religions. The nature of the food, its purity and quality, can be matters of great importance, with many restrictions on what may and may not be eaten. Orthodox Jews may follow a strictly Kosher diet, while vegans follow a diet which excludes all animal products, including eggs and milk.

Table 2.5 **Additives suspected of being linked to health problems**

Number	*Name or type*	*Suspected problems*
Colours		
E102, E104, E107, E110, E122, E123, E124, E127, E128, E131, E132, 133, E142, E151, 154, 155, E180	Coal tar dyes	May cause asthma, rashes, hyperactivity. Some have been linked to cancer in test animals
E120	Cochineal (insect extract)	Suspected of causing food intolerance
E150	Chemically treated burnt sugar	Some forms may damage genes. May reduce white blood cells and destroy vitamin B6
E160b	Annatto (tree-seed extract)	May cause skin rashes. Some types of annatto are banned
Preservatives		
E210, E211, E212, E213, E214, E215, E216, E217, E218, E219	Benzoates	May cause asthma, rashes, hyperactivity
E220, E221, E222, E223, E224, E226, E227	Sulphites	May provoke asthma. Destroy vitamin B1
E249, E250, E251, E252	Nitrates/nitrites	May produce nitrosamines which are linked to cancers. Can reduce blood oxygen levels

Antioxidants		
E310, E311, E312	Gallates	May cause liver damage and can irritate intestine
E320, E321	BHA and BHT	May cause rashes and hyperactivity. Linked to cancer in test animals
Emulsifiers, thickeners etc.		
E385	Calcium disodium EDTA	Possible link to liver damage in animals
E407	Carageenan (sea-weed extract)	Linked to ulcers in colon and foetal damage in test animals
E413	Tragacanth gum	May cause intolerance, and linked to liver damage in test animals
416	Karaya gum	May cause intolerance. Is a laxative so might reduce nutrient intake
430, 431, 432, 433, 434, 435, 436	Stearates and polysorbates	Possible link to skin and intestine inflammations, diarrhoea and possibly cancer
E450a, E450b, E450c	Di-, tri- and poly-phosphates	Possible link to kidney damage in test animals, can have laxative effect
Flavour enhancers		
620, 621, 622, 623	Glutamates	May cause dizziness and heart palpitations. Reproductive damage in test animals
627, 631, 635	Other enhancers	May aggravate gout and purine-sensitive problems
Improvers and bleaches		
924, 925, 926	Flour treating agents	May irritate stomach. Bleaches destroy natural vitamin E
Sweeteners		
	Saccharin	Linked to bladder cancer in animals
	Aspartame	Possible link to brain tumours. Dangerous to people suffering from phenylketonuria (an enzyme deficiency)

source: 2'3

For such people it can be difficult enough finding appropriate foods, even relying on the food labelling in shops. But, as we have shown, in the case of fast foods there are no labels to inspect. No information is given to help ensure you are eating what you want to eat. If for any reason you want to avoid certain products in your diet, you can't go to a fast food restaurant and be confident that you know what you can eat.

If the problem is serious for those with cultural restrictions, it can be worse for those who get physically ill if certain foods are eaten. Various disabling problems, such as asthma, migraine, nausea, eczema, skin rashes and

Table 2.6 **Milk products where you might not expect them**

Hot dogs
Turkey breast
Biriyani sauce
Sauces and relishes
Fried chicken breading
Frankfurters
Cold beef
Korma curry mix
Chicken nuggets

● For more facts on the contents of fast foods, see *Ingredients and Additives: The Details* at the back of this book.

sources: company labels, industry data

gastric upsets, can often be traced to the ingredients of foods. Hidden, unlabelled ingredients are a daily hazard to some food allergy sufferers. Called "food intolerances", these reactions can be found in response to such commonplace items as milk, wheat, eggs, shellfish, strawberries, chocolate and tea. Allergies can arise or can be worsened by the additives used to colour and to preserve food.

The number of people in the population who culturally or physically need to avoid certain food ingredients is large, as Table 2.4 indicates.

Table 2.5 is a checklist of additives which are suspected of either provoking allergic or intolerant reactions or of being linked to other diseases.

Tables 2.4 and 2.5 summarise the main reasons for food or additive avoidance known at present. But where exactly are these unrequested additions to the food? If you ask at the counter: "Do my fish and chips contain azo dye E110, known as sunset yellow FCF, or annatto E160b?" then what sort of an answer would you expect? Probably a blank look, at best. And yet the chances are that the fish and chips do indeed contain one or other of these colourants.

Table 2.7 **Pig products where you might not expect them**

Beef taco filling
Hamburgers
Cheese and onion quiche
Beef sausages
Hamburger buns
Turkey burgers
Chili-con-carne

● For more facts on the contents of fast foods, see *Ingredients and Additives: The Details* at the back of this book

sources: company labels, industry data

Table 2.8 **Egg products where you might not expect them**

Meat pies
Chicken breading
Coleslaw
Potato croquettes
Baked potato fillings
Hot sauces

● For more facts on the contents of fast foods, see *Ingredients and Additives: The Details* at the back of this book.

sources: company labels, industry data

Table 2.9 **Colouring agents where you might not expect them**

Burgers
Cornish pasties
Taramasalata
Salad cream
Tikkha mixes
Vegetable ghee
Soy sauce
Apple pies
Saveloys
Fish cakes
Fish batter
Tandoori mixes
Chinese noodles
Ice cream cones
Mustard
Fish fingers

● For more facts on the contents of fast foods, see *Ingredients and Additives: The Details* at the back of this book.

sources: company labels, industry data

Fast foods to check

Using the ingredients listings which we have compiled from catering packs, trade exhibitions and fast food dustbins, it is possible to identify the fast foods which might be taboo or hazardous to certain people.

Below are some of the ingredients that might present a problem for certain people. A detailed listing is given in *Ingredients and additives: the details*, at the back of this book.

Please remember that manufacturers are constantly changing their recipes and ingredients, so this book can only give an indication of the problems you face when you buy fast foods.

Until comprehensive ingredient listings are provided at the point where the food is being sold, customers have to rely on secondary information which might not always be as accurate as it should be. By not giving this information, food companies have only themselves to blame if their products are treated with suspicion or even avoided altogether by the public.

Table 2.10 **Artificial sweeteners where you might not expect them**

Coleslaw
Gherkins
Sweet & sour sauce
Salad cream
Noodles
Ice cream cones

● For more facts on the contents of fast foods, see *Ingredients and Additives: The Details* at the back of this book.

sources: company labels, industry data

Table 2.11 **Monosodium glutamate where you might not expect it**

Fried chicken coating
Chicken nuggets
Sausages
Pies
Cold ham
Soy sauce
Beef tacos
Hamburgers
Hot dogs
Saveloys
Pasties
Curry mixes
Barbecue sauce

● For more facts on the contents of fast foods, see *Ingredients and Additives: The Details* at the back of this book.

sources: company labels, industry data

Table 2.12 **Foods which might have unexpected animal products**

Animal fat
Cheese and tomato pizza
Nan mix
Burger bun
American cookies
Fish
Worcester sauce
Fish-derived flavouring
Instant noodles
Soy sauce
Insect-derived colouring
Low-fat sausages
Sweet and sour noodles
Caribbean pepper sauce

● For more facts on the contents of fast foods, see *Ingredients and Additives: The Details* at the back of this book.

sources: company labels, industry data

Chapter 3 The fast food nutrition line-up

Nutritionally, what makes a food good, bad or downright ugly depends on what it does to our bodies. Does it give us enough vitamins and minerals to keep us healthy? Does it give us too much fat and salt, perhaps increasing the risk of high blood pressure or heart disease?

This chapter takes a look at how the good, the bad and the ugly in fast foods line up nutritionally. Which is high in salt or a good source of fibre? Which has 21 teaspoons of fat in it and which has 12 teaspoons of sugar? And which can provide a good helping of vitamin A or vitamin C?

This is where we compare the better and the worse in fast food catering, graded on the scale that matters most: your health. We take the main nutritional recommendations and ask how the foods in our fast food shops and take-away restaurants stand up to a detailed analysis.

Calorie counting

For more calorie counts, see the nutritional tables towards the back of this book.

Table 3.1 gives a checklist of some fast foods, showing the calorie count for an average portion.

Remember, fat provides more than twice as many calories weight for weight as sugar, starch or protein. High-fat foods are usually the high calorie foods. And watch the sauces: a tablespoon of vinegar has about 1 Calorie while a tablespoon of mayonnaise has as much as 140 Calories.

Table 3.1 **A fast check-out on calories**

Some single-item high calorie fast foods

Item	*Calories in an average portion*
Pizzas: smaller dishes	550-850
larger dishes	800-1500
Sweet and sour pork	600-1100
Special fried rice	550-950
Spare ribs in barbecue sauce	550-850
Meat curry or meat biriyani	500-950
Spud-U-Like potato, cheese & egg filling	500-720

Battered ¼ chicken	600-650
Battered plaice	500-650
6oz Pasty	460-550
4oz Pork pie	400-450
Wimpy halfpounder	830
Wimpy ¼-pounder with cheese	540
McDonald ¼-pounder with cheese	500
Burger King Double Whopper	890
Burger King Whopper with cheese	760
McDonald Big Mac	550
Burger King Chicken in bun	690
Wimpy Chicken in bun	510
Wimpy Beanburger with cheese	520
Kentucky Fried Chicken - 3 pieces	630
Fries	
McDonald	290
Wimpy	275
Burger King	225
Kentucky Fried Chicken	260
Shakes	
McDonald	360-390
Wimpy	260
Burger King	320
And some low-calorie fast food items	
Pizzaland corn on the cob	155
Kentucky Fried Chicken corn on the cob	176
Spud-U-Like potato with cottage cheese	280-330
Kentucky Fried Chicken small jacket potato	150
Kentucky Fried Chicken coleslaw	100
Kentucky Fried Chicken barbeque beans	85-105
Taco Bell Tostada*	180
Taco Bell Taco*	185
Taco Bell Nacho*	180
Taco Bell Mexican rice*	180
Wimpy plain burger	260
McDonald plain burger	255
Burger King plain burger	275
McDonald Chicken McNuggets (6)	265
British Rail ham sandwich	225

source: LFC and company data * US company data

Burning off the calories

If you eat more calories than you burn you gain weight. Eat less than you burn and you lose weight. The only way to eat a lot of calories and yet not put on weight is to take exercise. But not just the occasional walk to the shops. It takes serious exercise to burn up calories and Table 3.2 shows what we mean. The table shows how much extra activity an average adult would have to exert to burn up those extra fast food calories.

Table 3.2 **How long it may take to burn the calories**

Snack	*Calories*	*Playing squash*	*Swimming slow crawl*	*Walking 2 m.p.h.*	*Reading this book*
Wimpy white coffee (no sugar)	18	1min	2min	6min	14min
McDonald cola (medium)	120	9min	15min	41min	1h 32min
Wimpy chips	275	20min	34min	1h 35min	3h 32min
Burger King fried apple pie	305	23min	38min	1h 45min	3h 55min
McDonald strawberry milk shake	380	28min	47min	2h 11min	4h 52min
4oz Pork pie	440	32min	54min	2h 31min	5h 40min

source 4.1

Fat finding

Many people are eating more fat than they need and more than is good for their health. The amount of fat in the average diet has been increasing over the last few decades so that it now provides an average 43% of our daily calories.

Certain types of fat – those rich in *saturated fatty acids* – are known to be particularly closely related to the risk of getting heart disease. Others – those rich in *polyunsaturated fatty acids* – can actually be a health bonus. The general advice is to keep fats as a proportion of total calories at around 30 to 35% and to make sure that the saturated fats are well under half total fat consumption.

For more fat facts, see the nutrition tables towards the back of this book.

If fatty food is your worry then be wary of most fast foods. Nearly all of them have fat or oil in them and some are swimming in the stuff. Table 3.3 shows how some single menu items can pile up the fat on your plate with a lot of it saturated fat.

Deep fat frying

Most chips and french fries, battered fish and many other fast foods are cooked by immersing the raw or pre-cooked food in very hot fat. The food absorbs some of the fat, and so when you eat the food you will eat some of the fat it was cooked in. French fries and chips, especially the thin-cut sorts, can absorb a lot of fat. Thicker chips, having less surface area for their weight, tend to absorb proportionally less fat. But many chips are pre-cooked in fat and then cooked again just before serving. This double exposure adds yet more fat to each chip.

Apart from the quantity of fat, there is also the question

Table 3.3 **Fat levels in single-item fast foods**

Some of the highest-fat fast foods		
Item	*Total fat (saturated)*	*Proportion of calories from fat*
Wimpy Halfpounder	54g (27g)	59%
McDonald Big Mac	28g (10g)	45%
Burger King Whopper	36g (12g)	52%
Kentucky Fried Chicken, 4 pieces	45g (12g*)	58%
Wimpy ¼-pounder with cheese	33g (15g)	51%
McDonald ¼-pounder with cheese	25g (12g)	46%
McDonald Filet-o-Fish	26g (7g)	56%
Jumbo 4oz sausage	30g (11g)	75%
Saveloy	20g (7g)	65%
6oz Pasty	33g (10g)	56%
Fat in regular items		
Hamburgers		
Wimpy burger	10g	
McDonald burger	10g	
Burger King burger	12g	
Kentucky Fried Chicken, 1 piece	11g	
Fries		
McDonald regular	16g	
Wimpy chips	14g	
Kentucky Fried Chicken regular	11g	
Burger King regular	13g	
Shakes		
Wimpy	7g	
McDonald	11g	
Burger King	11g	

sources: company data where company is named
* US data

of quality. The fat used for deep fat frying varies from place to place. Some large companies favour vegetable oil, others favour animal fat. We list the larger companies' preferences, and some of the oils used by smaller companies, in Table 3.4 below. Deep fried food bought in the north of England is more likely to have been cooked in animal fat while deep fat frying in vegetable oil is more common in the south. But even when vegetable oil is used it may be hydrogenated, an industrial process which increases the saturated fat content. Or it may be a type of vegetable oil rich in saturated fats, such as palm oil.

Salt sellers

A small amount of salt is found naturally in food and in some parts of the world this is the only salt eaten in the diet. But in Western culture extra salt is usually added to many

Table 3.4 **The fats in the fryers**

	Fats used	*Estimated % saturated fat*
McDonald french fries	Mainly beef fat	45-55%
McDonald other items	Vegetable oil	25%
Wimpy – all items	Vegetable oil	15%
Burger King french fries	Mainly beef fat	45-55%
Burger King other items	Vegetable oil	20%
Kentucky Fried Chicken – all items	Hardened soya fat	23%
Independents	Beef fat	45-55%
	Lard	40-45%
	Palm fat	45-55%
	Cotton-seed oil	26-32%
	Ground-nut oil	20%
	Corn oil	14-18%
	Soya oil	14%
	Sunflower oil	12-15%
	Rapeseed oil	7-10%

sources: company data where company is named

Table 3.5 **Some single-item salt shakers**

Item	*Salt (g)*
Wimpy Halfpounder	5
McDonald Big Mac	2-3
Burger King Whopper with cheese	3
Wimpy ¼-pounder with cheese	3
Wimpy Beanburger with cheese	3
McDonald ¼-pounder with cheese	2-3
Burger King Chicken in bun	3-4
Kentucky Fried Chicken, 3 pieces	3-4
Hot dog in roll	3
Chicken pie	2-3
Chinese fried rice	2-4
Prawn Chow Mein	2-4
Soy sauce – 2 teaspoons	2

source: company data where company is named

savoury foods. Many people boil their vegetables in salted water, cook pasta in salted water, add salt to their recipes and also sprinkle it on the food before eating.

For more salt surprises, see the nutrition tables towards the back of this book.

Food manufacturers are equally free and easy with the salt-cellar, each year shaking an estimated *6lbs of salt for every person in the UK* into processed food.

The result is a possible threat to health. It used to be

thought that the rise in blood pressure as one got older was a natural phenomenon. But it has been found that in some areas of the world there are people who show no rise in blood pressure as they age. These people eat very little salt. So salt has been identified as a possible source of blood pressure problems which affect millions of people in the UK alone and which have led to a recommendation by the World Health Organisation that salt intake should be limited. (It is, in fact, *sodium* intake that needs to be limited. Salt is a common form of sodium, sodium chloride.)

Most people actually need less than 5gm of salt each day - a teaspoonful - which is the amount the World Health Organisation suggests as a maximum for adults. *The amount naturally present in food would be enough by itself.* But in Britain an estimated 12gm per person is eaten on average each day, and if you eat fast foods that figure may be even higher.

Table 3.5 is a checklist of the salt in some fast food items *before* any extra is added at the counter.

For more fibre figures, see the nutrition tables towards the back of this book.

Fibre fillers

Dietary fibre is the part of fruit, vegetables, grains, seed and pulses which is not broken down in the stomach and so passes through as waste. However, it is not a waste to eat it! Fibre performs a very useful role in the gut. High fibre diets are associated to prevent some cancers and heart disease as well.

There are several sorts of dietary fibre found in different quantities in different foods, including fruit, vegetables, cereals and pulses. Some sorts are good at bulking out the gut and relieving constipation and some are good at absorbing cholesterol, so lowering cholesterol in the blood.

Bran – the husk of wheat grains – is promoted as a dietary supplement. But pure fibre in this form may have some bad effects along with the possible benefits; notably that it can prevent the full absorption of useful minerals. When bran is eaten in food rich in minerals (e.g. in the bran's original whole wheat form) then this should not be a problem. But if bran is taken as a fibre supplement in an otherwise poor, mineral-scarce diet then it may just worsen the potential deficiency and do as much harm as good in the long run.

Table 3.6 **Good fibre buys**

Item	*Dietary fibre (g)*
Wimpy Beanburger (with brown bun)	16
Wimpy brown bun alone	6
Pizzaland wholemeal pizza	12
Large shish kebab with salad	6
Spud-U-Like plain potato	7-8
Spud-U-Like potato with beans	15-16
4oz Mushy peas	9
6oz Chips	4
4oz Chapati	4
3oz Pitta bread	3
Taco Bell Bean Burrito (4oz)	9 (est.)

There are several ways of measuring fibre, which result in different figures for these food items. The values reported in this book are those which match the national recommendation for 30g per day average for adults. McDonald published data uses a different method giving higher values that cannot be directly compared with the values on this table or the 30g recommended average.

source: company data where company is named

Although nutritionists have recommended a national average of 30gm dietary fibre each day, the amount needed differs from person to person. Because of the variety of types of fibre, and the range of individual needs and appetites, it is more important to ask, *"Am I eating plenty of fruit and vegetables, wholegrain foods and pulses?"* rather than *"Am I getting 30gm today?"*.

Fast food does not have a good reputation on the fibre front, as neither meat, fish, milk nor soft drinks have any fibre (unless as an additive). White rolls, buns and pastries are usually low-fibre, too. But there are some good sources for dietary fibre among the fast foods and Table 3.6 shows which these are.

Sweet teasers

Most fast food in our survey was savoury. This doesn't mean it had no sugar in it as quite a lot of manufacturers put sugar in savoury foods to enhance the taste.

For more sugar statistics, see the nutrition tables towards the back of this book.

However, the sweet fast food items we analysed were not just sweet but *very* sweet. A large cola, for example, had fourteen spoonfuls of sugar in it (and nutritionally had no other value at all).

Table 3.7 shows some examples of the sugar levels in fast foods.

Table 3.7 **Little sweeties**

Item	*% sugar*	*Teaspoons**
Sausage roll	4%	1
Cornish pasty	3%	1
Onion bhajis	5%	2
Cheese & tomato pizza	3%	2
Big frankfurter	5%	2
Spare ribs in sauce	4%	3
Quarterpounder in sesame bun	6%	3
Sweet & sour chicken with egg fried rice	4%	8
Deep-fried apple pie	15%	3
Milk shake (small)	8-12%	3
Milk shake (large)	8-12%	8
Cola (large)	11%	14

* at 4-5 grams sugar per teaspoon

Essentials: the minerals and vitamins

There is evidence from dietary surveys that some people in Britain today may be getting insufficient quantities of certain essential nutrients in their diet (see Chapter 5).

We took four of the nutrients which the surveys found were lacking in some people's diets – *iron, calcium, vitamin A and vitamin C* – and asked whether fast foods scored well for these four essentials.

Iron Iron is essential for healthy blood and without it we would quickly become anaemic. For people who need the most iron in their diet – teenage girls and pregnant women – the target for a balanced diet is an average of over half a milligram (0.5mg) of iron for every 100 Calories, and a total of over 12mg in a day. (Incidentally, cups of tea can reduce the ability to absorb iron whereas orange juice can increase the absorption of iron.)

As there are many fast foods, including fish and chips, pasties, milk shakes, and soft drinks, which contain less than 0.5mg per 100 Calories, it is important that other foods in the diet are well up on the average for iron content.

We took as a "good source" of iron any food item that had twice the average level needed, i.e. around 1mg per 100 Calories, and also had in total at least 20 to 25% of daily iron needs, i.e. about 3mg in all.

For more iron facts, see the nutritional tables towards the back of this book.

Table 3.8 **Fast foods: useful sources of iron**

Item	*Total iron*	*Iron/100 Calories*
Large shish kebab & salad	4mg	0.9mg
Spud-U-Like potato with baked beans	3-4mg	1.1mg
Spud-U-Like potato with chili-con-carne	4mg	1.1mg
Quarterpounder	3mg	1.0mg
Burger King burger	3mg	1.1mg
Taco Bell beef burrito*	4-5mg	1.0mg
Pizza Hut ½ a 13" cheese pizza*	7-9mg	1.1mg
Onion bhajis	5mg	1.4mg
Fried egg roll	4mg	1.6mg
Fried bacon roll	3mg	1.4mg
Jamaican patty	6mg	1.4mg
Chicken Madras	10-11mg	2.4mg
Lamb curry	14mg	2.7mg

sources: company data if company is named (* US data)

We searched through all the published material we could find, as well as our own analyses, and table 3.8 shows the fast food items we found that could provide a rich and useful helping of iron.

Despite analysing over 140 fast food items only a few can be awarded the cast-iron medal for good iron value. This doesn't mean you cannot get enough iron from other items; for example you can get over 5mg in a Wimpy Halfpounder. But you may have to munch through a lot of calories and fat to get that iron.

Calcium Calcium is essential for healthy bones and teeth. Foods rich in calcium include milk, cheese, fortified white flour, pulses and some vegetables. People with high calcium needs include pregnant and breastfeeding women. They need as much as 45 to 50mg per 100 Calories, and a total of 1200mg in total as a daily average.

As many fast foods fall below the 45 to 50mg/100 Calorie levels, including meat, fish, potatoes and soft drinks other than milk shakes, we took as our criteria for "good sources" of calcium a figure of double the density, i.e. around 90 to 100mg/100 Calories, and at least 20 to 25% of total daily need, i.e. around 250 to 300mg or more in a serving.

What items of fast food could provide that amount of calcium? We looked at over 140 food items and Table 3.9

shows the ones we found.

Table 3.9 **Fast foods: useful sources of calcium**

Item	*Total calcium*	*Calcium/ 100 Calories*
McDonald milk	240mg	115mg
McDonald milk shakes	515-525mg	132-147mg
Burger King whole milk	290mg	184mg
Burger King 2% milk	297mg	245mg
Pizza Hut ½ a 13" cheese pizza*	800mg	118mg
Spud-U-Like potato with cheddar	700mg	143mg
Thin crust cheese & tomato pizza	1028mg	167mg
Jacket potato, cheese & onion filling	975mg	212mg
Cheese salad sandwiches	500-550mg	145-155mg
Beefburger in bun (microwave)	653mg	130mg
Large shish kebab & salad	492mg	102mg
Milk shakes (small)	200-250mg	190-220mg

source: company data if company is named (* US data)

Again, there is not a lot to get excited about in this list. There are not many high calcium foods for expectant mothers here. Most of the items listed rely on the milk or cheese to supply the calcium, or else use fortified flour. (McDonald's milk shakes are richer in calcium than one might expect from the milk alone, probably as a result of adding extra dried skimmed milk powder to the mix).

For more calcium counters, see the nutritional tables towards the back of this book.

Vitamin A Essential to healthy sight, vitamin A is also thought to help prevent the development of cancer. Some vitamin A can be found in butter and cheese while some gets added to margarine. Richer sources are to be found among vegetables, especially carrots and spinach, and in liver.

Recommended average levels range up to 750ug (ug stands for microgram, a thousandth of a milligram) per day for teenagers, and more for breastfeeding women. The average needed in most people's diet is around 25 to 35ug per 100 Calories. Meat, potatoes and soft drinks have very little vitamin A, so other foods would have to be relatively rich sources to compensate. We took as our criteria for a "good source" a level of 70ug/100 Calories, and an overall

For more vitamin A values, see the nutrition tables towards the back of this book.

contribution of 20 to 25% or more of the daily needs, i.e. 150 to 200ug or more per serving.

Table 3.10 **Fast foods: useful sources of vitamin A**

Item	*Total vitamin A*	*Vitamin A/ 100 Calories*
Taco Bell tostadas*	est 500ug	est 300ug
Taco Bell burrito supreme*	est 550ug	est 100ug

* US company data

Just two items seemed to be rich sources of vitamin A. There was one runner-up (Wimpy Beanburger with cheese) and there were a few also-rans (cheese rolls, cheese sandwiches and cheese pizzas, depending on how generous the cheese is).

Fortunately for concerned fast food customers the answer to their vitamin A problems might be fairly easy – eat a carrot. Not only does a single, average-sized carrot provide good dietary fibre, it also provides a healthy helping of vitamin A in one cheap and easily-found stick. However, recent evidence suggests there are various types of vitamin A and carrots alone will not give all the types you might need. Other sources of vitamin A, such as cheese, liver and green vegetables, should also be eaten.

Vitamin C This vitamin plays a role in many of the body's functions and is believed by some to help the body resist common infections. Not much vitamin C is stored in the body, so we each need to keep up a good supply. Good sources are fruits, especially citrus fruits, and vegetables, especially the cabbage family and potatoes. But vitamin C is easily lost in cooking – heat destroys it and water washes it out of the food. Most people are recommended to get around 30mg each day on average, but pregnant and breastfeeding women should aim for twice this level.

As many fast foods, including meat, bread, milk shakes and pastry, contain little or no vitamin C you need to be sure that other foods you eat have vitamin C at useful levels. We took as our criteria of a "good source" of vitamin C one that is over double the average needed by most people, i.e. around 3mg/100 Calories or more, and that supplies a good 25% of average daily needs, i.e. 7 to 8mg or more in a portion.

In our list of fast foods we found just a few that meet the criteria as a rich source of vitamin C.

Table 3.11 **Fast foods: useful sources of vitamin C**

Item	*Total vitamin C*	*Vitamin C/ 100 Calories*
Wimpy beanburger with cheese	18mg	3mg
Wimpy orange juice	65mg	107mg
McDonald orange juice	51mg	57mg
Burger King orange juice	71mg	87mg
Kentucky Fried Chicken coleslaw	19mg	18mg
Taco Bell various burritos*	15-16mg	3-4mg
Spud-U-Like potato, plain	12mg	4mg
6oz chips	10mg	2-3mg
Spare ribs in sauce[1]	26mg	3mg

[1] see text
source: company data if company is named (* US data)

For more vitamin C values, see the nutritional tables towards the back of this book.

A few of the items we analysed here had higher levels of vitamin C than one would expect from the usual recipes. This is probably because vitamin C has been used as an additive to preserve the food during long storage. Some scientists have raised doubts about whether synthetic vitamin C used as an additive has the full range of benefits which vitamin C eaten in a natural food source would have.

Chips – the chunky variety – just about squeeze into our criteria as a "good source" of vitamin C. Their levels of vitamin C will depend on whether the potatoes used are new or old ones, whether they have been pre-fried, and so cooked twice, and the degree of fat absorption. New potatoes have more vitamin C, as do potatoes that are cooked only once. Potatoes which have absorbed less fat will not have the vitamin C swimming around in too many fatty calories.

French fries, because they are thinner and so have more surface area for their weight, absorb more fat in cooking and so do not make our list. The portions are usually small and the calories from the fat too high to make them a really useful source.

We have seen that only a few fast food items are really rich sources of iron, calcium and vitamins A and C. To survive nutritionally on fast food you need to eat a variety of foods. *But these may not be available on a single fast food menu.* The temptation is to fill up on what *is* available, to the detriment of your present and future health.

Other essential nutrients

Besides iron, calcium and vitamins A and C, there are other essential nutrients which might be lacking in fast foods, such as the B vitamins and several essential trace minerals. The evidence suggests that fast foods may be short on:

- Vitamin B6, which is easily destroyed during processing and cooking. Everyone needs this vitamin but pregnant women and women taking oral contraceptives are particularly advised to ensure they get good supplies. Go for fresh chicken, fish and jacket potatoes with bean fillings.
- Folic acid, which everyone needs, is also easily destroyed during processing and cooking. Go for green vegetables, beans, peas and liver.
- Vitamin E is an essential nutrient which is found in fresh vegetable oils, nuts, oily fish like herring, mackerel and tuna fish, eggs and wholegrains.
- Copper, magnesium, manganese and zinc are all minerals of which you need small but reliable amounts. These minerals, which tend to be found in rich concentrations in wholemeal breads, grains, nuts, pulses and eggs, may be deficient in fast food diets.

Chapter 4 **A fast look at forty items**

Of course, no single fast food item can provide everything you need nutritionally. You have to choose a variety of items for a balanced diet. But one of the main characteristics of fast food outlets is their limited range of menu items. (That, after all, is why their food service is fast.)

So if you eat fast food regularly - and nearly a third of the 350 fast food eaters we talked to in Peckham, London, said they ate fast foods *every day* - what chance do you have of getting a balanced diet?

Is the fast food many people buy and eat for the main meal of the day anywhere near a healthy balance nutritionally? We asked fast food eaters in our survey: *What is your main meal of the day?* Table 4.1 shows the sort of main meals eaten by regular fast food eaters.

Table 4.1 **Fast food main meals of the day**

Examples of fast food main meals in our Peckham, London, survey of 350 fast food eaters.
Fish and chips
Chicken and chips
Cod roe and chips
Burger, chips and shake
Chips
Kebab
Chicken
Corn-on-the-cob
Chicken, chips, coleslaw
Pancake roll, chips, soft drink
Two burgers
Pie
Chips and onion
Burger
Chicken, chips, cheesecake
Sausage, pasty, chips
Pie and chips
Burger, fries, nuggets, apple pie
Burger and juice
Fish, burger, chips, soft drink
Fish & chips, apple pie, ice cream
Cheese egg burger

source: LFC survey 1'6

Can *any* of these choices be considered a balanced meal? Certainly some of the less expensive choices cannot offer a balance. For example, you would need to eat around *sixty* bags of french fries to get anywhere near your daily calcium requirement, but by then you might have eaten at least five times as many calories as you need and be on the way to a serious weight problem.

Fish and chips, burgers and chips, chicken and fries – do these combinations get nearer the "balanced meal" mark, or are they still short on what you need from a main meal? In the following pages we analyse a range of fast foods and ask *Are there problems with this food? If you eat this food regularly, what else would you need to balance your daily diet?*

We have co-operated with Southwark Public Protection to have Public Analysts examine some 40 fast food and take-away food products, and we have combined their results with other published sources to show

- what you might be getting in a typical dish
- what you might be missing
- how to make it balance

We judged the food to be high in *fat* if it exceeded the government's recommended average level of around 35% of the calories from fat, and we judged the *saturated fat* to be high if it exceeded the recommended average of 10 to 15% of calories from saturated fat. We judged the *salt* to be high if the sodium levels were more than around a gram per 1000 Calories *before any salt is added at the counter.* We indicate if the food is a *good* source of any nutrient (more than the average needed for the calories the food supplies) or if the food provides a smaller but nonetheless *useful amount* of a nutrient. We also indicate whether the food is likely to be *short* on some essential nutrients that will have to be found elsewhere.

Of the fast food dishes we analysed, we found:

- nearly three quarters of the dishes were high in fats, many having as much as 60% of the calories in the form of fat. This is nearly double the government's recommended level.
- over half the savoury items were high in salt, even before they reached the counter.
- only six items could be called fairly well-balanced (being significantly short on less than four essential nutrients).

A reminder Products can change, ingredients can change, cooking methods can change and portion sizes can change. Our findings are based on typical products bought in south London during 1988. Although the large fast food chains stick to the same recipes across the country, the small independents tend to follow local tradition. For example deep frying is more often done in animal fat in the north of Britain and in vegetable fat in the south[4/1].

For more detailed nutritional information see the previous chapter in this book which looks at the best and worst scoring products. See the tables at the back which give the nutritional details and the additives found in these foods.

Sweet and sour chicken with egg fried rice

Independent take-away

The portions we looked at weighed on average a total of 912gm, around 2lb. It was a very large meal for one person.

Calories: 2050

For the calories this food provides, it is high in ***fats*** and ***salt***

It is a good source of ***protein, iron*** and ***calcium***

It gives useful amounts of ***dietary fibre, zinc, vitamin B12, vitamin B6, vitamin A, niacin*** and ***vitamin C***

It is short on ***vitamin E, folic acid, vitamin B1, vitamin B2*** and ***vitamin D***

We found the colouring *tartrazine* in this meal, probably from the sauce.

This was a big meal for a big appetite and would provide an average adult with around three-quarters of their day's total calorie needs. The meal had nearly a quarter of a pound of pure fat in it. This makes it important to ensure that the missing nutrients are found in a low-calorie form.

Nutritionally, you should add to your diet some rich sources of the nutrients listed as insufficient, while not adding too much to the overall calories you eat. A balanced diet means plenty of fruit and vegetables and plenty of starchy foods, plus some dairy products and some lean meat and fish (or meat substitutes like beans, nuts, eggs, etc). A good balance might be achieved by adding to your diet foods rich in the missing nutrients, such as: *green and red vegetables, sweet potato, fruit, lean red meat, skimmed milk, nuts (and sunshine for vitamin D).*

Fried fish, ackee, rice and peas

Independent take-away

The portions we looked at weighed on average a total of 609gm, over 1lb 5oz.

Calories: 1230

For the calories this food provides, it is high in ***fats*** and ***salt***

It is a good source of ***protein*** and ***calcium***

It gives useful amounts of ***iron, vitamin B1, vitamin B2, niacin, dietary fibre, zinc, folic acid, vitamin B12, vitamin B6*** and ***vitamin E***

It is short on ***vitamin D, vitamin A*** and ***vitamin C***

Although fairly oily, this dish was not high in saturated fats. Its overall balance of nutrients was fairly good. Some fresh fruit or salad would complete the balance.

Nutritionally, you should add to your diet some rich sources of the nutrients listed as insufficient, without adding too much to the fat you eat. A balanced diet means plenty of fruit and vegetables and plenty of starchy foods, plus some dairy products and some lean meat and fish (or meat substitutes like beans, nuts, eggs, etc).

A good balance might be achieved by adding to your diet foods rich in the missing nutrients, such as: *green and red vegetables, fruit (and sunshine for vitamin D).*

Cod and chips

Independent take-away

The portions we looked at weighed on average a total of 477gm, just over 1lb.

Calories: 1055

For the calories this food provides, it is high in ***fats***

It is a good source of ***protein, calcium (mostly in the batter)*** and ***vitamins B6*** and ***B12***

It gives useful amounts of ***vitamin C, iron, vitamin B1, niacin, dietary fibre*** and ***zinc***

It is short on ***vitamin A, folic acid, vitamin E, vitamin B2*** and ***vitamin D***

We found colouring agent *tartrazine* (E102) which was almost certainly being used in the batter. Other products may have colouring agent *annatto* in the batter (and possibly in the chips' soaking solution) and the water-retaining agent *sodium polyphosphate* in the fish.

Nutritionally, you should add to your diet some rich sources of the nutrients listed as insufficient, while not adding too much to the fat you eat. A balanced diet means plenty of fruit and vegetables and plenty of starchy foods, plus some dairy products and some lean meat and fish (or meat substitutes like beans, nuts, eggs, etc). A good balance might be achieved by adding to your diet foods rich in the missing nutrients, such as: *green and red vegetables, liver, lean meats, nuts, wholegrains and wholemeal bread, sweet potato, beans and lentils (and sunshine for vitamin D).*

Beanburger in bun with chips (fries)

Multinational

The portions we looked at weighed on average a total of 338gm, around 12oz.

Calories: 925

For the calories this food provides, it is high in ***fats***

It is a good source of ***protein, calcium, vitamin A, niacin*** and ***dietary fibre***

It gives useful amounts of ***vitamin C, iron, vitamin B1, vitamin B6, folic acid*** and ***zinc***

It is short on ***vitamin B2, vitamin D, vitamin B12*** and ***vitamin E***

Nutritionally, you should add to your diet some rich sources of the nutrients listed as insufficient, while not adding too much to the fat you eat. A balanced diet means plenty of fruit and vegetables and plenty of starchy foods, plus some dairy products and some lean meat and fish (or meat substitutes like beans, nuts, eggs, etc). A good balance might be achieved by adding to your diet foods rich in the missing nutrients, such as: *skimmed milk, eggs, lean meats, tuna fish, sweet potato, wholegrains and wholemeal bread, nuts seeds (and sunshine for vitamin D).*

Chicken and chips

Independent take-away

The portions we looked at weighed on average a total of 309gm, around 11oz.

Calories: 890

For the calories this food provides, it is high in ***fats, saturated fats*** and ***salt***

It is a good source of ***protein, niacin*** and ***vitamin B6***

It gives useful amounts of ***vitamin C, iron, vitamin B1, zinc, calcium, dietary fibre*** and ***vitamin B2***

It is short on ***vitamin A, folic acid, vitamin B12, vitamin E*** and ***vitamin D***

Without chips, this dish would be significantly short on vitamin C and dietary fibre.

If the chicken has a coating of flour and crumb then the flour may add some useful calcium, but may well contain *monosodium glutamate* and a colouring agent, such as *tartrazine* or *annatto*. In some instances the chicken may have been soaked in a solution of *sodium polyphosphate* which helps it to absorb water, adding a lot to its overall weight but nothing to its nutritional value.

Nutritionally, you should add to your diet some rich sources of the nutrients listed as insufficient, while not adding too much to the fat you eat. A balanced diet means plenty of fruit and vegetables and plenty of starchy foods, plus some dairy products and some lean meat and fish (or meat substitutes like beans, nuts, eggs, etc). A good balance might be achieved by adding to your diet foods rich in the missing nutrients, such as: *green and red vegetables, liver, oily fish, eggs, nuts, wholegrains and wholemeal bread (and sunshine for vitamin D).*

Spare ribs in sauce

Independent take-away

The portions we looked at weighed on average 325gm, over 11oz.

Calories: 830

For the calories this food provides, it is high in ***fats, saturated fats*** and ***salt***

It is a good source of ***protein, calcium, zinc, vitamin C, vitamin B1, niacin*** and ***vitamin B12***

It gives useful amounts of ***vitamin B2, dietary fibre*** and ***vitamin B6***

It is short on ***iron, folic acid, vitamin D, vitamin A*** and ***vitamin E***

We found the colouring *sunset yellow* in this dish, probably from the sauce. The high level of salt might be partially due to sodium found in the flavour enhancer *monosodium glutamate* or to soya sauce which is part of the barbecue sauce and very high in salt.

We found more vitamin C than we expected, possibly from the tomato used in the sauce but more probably from the use of canned ingredients which had added vitamin C as an antioxidant to prevent the fats going rancid or the added colour fading.

Nutritionally, you should add to your diet some rich sources of the nutrients listed as insufficient. A balanced diet means plenty of fruit and vegetables and plenty of starchy foods, plus some dairy products and some lean meat and fish (or meat substitutes like beans, nuts, eggs, etc).

A good balance might be achieved by adding to your diet foods rich in the missing nutrients, such as: *green and red vegetables, beans, wholegrains and wholemeal bread, milk, nuts, seeds (and sunshine for vitamin D).*

Saveloy and chips

Independent take-away

The portions we looked at weighed on average a total of 407gm, over 14oz.

Calories: 795

For the calories this food provides, it is high in ***fats***

It is a good source of ***protein, niacin*** and ***vitamin C***

It gives useful amounts of ***dietary fibre, zinc, vitamin B1, iron, calcium*** and ***vitamin B6***

It is short on ***vitamin E, folic acid, vitamin A, vitamin B2, vitamin D*** and ***vitamin B12***

We found the colouring *red 2G* in this meal, probably from the saveloy.

The vitamin C in this meal was higher than expected. Potatoes are the likely source of the vitamin C, and new potatoes, freshly cut and cooked, will have the most. But some meat products, including saveloys, now use vitamin C to act as an antioxidant. This acts to stop the fat from going rancid and the added colour from fading over long storage periods.

Nutritionally, you should add to your diet some rich sources of the nutrients listed as insufficient, while not adding too much to the overall calories you eat. A balanced diet means plenty of fruit and vegetables and plenty of starchy foods, plus some dairy products and some lean meat and fish (or meat substitutes like beans, nuts, eggs, etc). A good balance might be achieved by adding to your diet foods rich in the missing nutrients, such as: *green and red vegetables, sweet potato, fruit, milk, nuts, cod roe (and sunshine for vitamin D).*

Doner kebab with salad

Independent take-away

The portions we looked at weighed on average a total of 265gm, just over 9oz.

Calories: 745

For the calories this food provides, it is high in ***fats, saturated fats*** and ***salt***

It is a good source of ***protein, zinc, niacin*** and ***vitamin B12***

It gives useful amounts of ***iron, vitamin B1, vitamin B2, vitamin C, dietary fibre, calcium*** and ***vitamin B6***

It is short on ***vitamin A, folic acid, vitamin E*** and ***vitamin D***

Our samples had high amounts of saturated fat and surprisingly little vitamin C. Some doner kebab meat has less fat, and the vitamin C could be improved with a generous portion of salad (e.g. shredded cabbage, tomato). Shop around.

Nutritionally, you should add to your diet some rich sources of the nutrients listed as insufficient, while not adding too much to the fat you eat. A balanced diet means plenty of fruit and vegetables and plenty of starchy foods, plus some dairy products and some lean meat and fish (or meat substitutes like beans, nuts, eggs, etc). A good balance might be achieved by adding to your diet foods rich in the missing nutrients, such as: *green and red vegetables, sweet potato, fruit, nuts, wholegrains and wholemeal bread, tuna fish (and sunshine for vitamin D).*

Cheeseburger and chips
Multinational

The portions we looked at weighed on average a total of 263gm, just over 9oz.

Calories: 685

For the calories this food provides, it is high in ***fats*** and ***saturated fats***

It is a good source of ***protein, calcium, vitamin B1, niacin*** and ***vitamin B12***

It gives useful amounts of ***iron, vitamin C, dietary fibre*** and ***zinc***

It is short on ***vitamin A, folic acid, vitamin B2, vitamin E, vitamin D*** and ***vitamin B6***

If the chips are fried in a vegetable oil like corn or soya oil the overall saturated fat levels may not get too high. But if the chips are fried in animal fat, or a more saturated vegetable oil, then the saturated fat levels in this dish could get excessive. For more on frying fats see Chapter 3.

We were surprised to find two colouring agents, *quinoline yellow* and *sunset yellow*, in this dish. It is possible they were in the chips' soaking solution, the cheese or even the burger meat. Cheeseburger cheese is usually a highly processed cheese with various emulsifying salts and colouring agents in it, but not usually these azo dyes. Cheap "economy" burgers, which can be bought in cash-and-carry wholesalers in cans or deep frozen, may have colouring and polyphosphate salts and may not be all beef or even all meat.

Nutritionally, you should add to your diet some rich sources of the nutrients listed as insufficient, while not adding too much to the fat you eat. A balanced diet means plenty of fruit and vegetables and plenty of starchy foods, plus some dairy products and some lean meat and fish (or meat substitutes like beans, nuts, eggs, etc). A good balance might be achieved by adding to your diet foods rich in the missing nutrients, such as: *green and red vegetables, sweet potato, liver, lean meat, skimmed milk, nuts, wholegrains and wholemeal bread, tuna fish (and sunshine for vitamin D).*

Cheese and tomato thin-crust pizza

Independent take-away

The portions we looked at weighed on average a total of 246gm, just under 9oz.

Calories: 615

For the calories this food provides, it is high in ***salt***

It is a good source of ***protein, niacin, vitamin B12*** and ***calcium***

It gives useful amounts of ***iron, zinc, vitamin B1, vitamin D, vitamin A, dietary fibre, vitamin C, vitamin B2*** and ***vitamin E***

It is short on ***vitamin B6*** and ***folic acid***

This dish is fairly low in fat (20% calories from fat) but what fat there is comes from the cheese and so is over 50% saturated fat. It was also rather too salty, probably also due to the cheese. But the cheese gives valuable calcium, and overall this is one of the better take-aways we examined for getting balanced nutrition.

Nutritionally, you should add to your diet some rich sources of the nutrients listed as insufficient, e.g. *green vegetables, fish.*

Pie and mash with liquor

Independent take-away

The portions we looked at weighed on average a total of 832gm, nearly 2lb, but over 80% of this is water.

Calories: 600

For the calories this food provides, it is high in ***salt***

It is a good source of ***protein, iron, calcium, niacin, dietary fibre*** and ***vitamin C***

It gives useful amounts of ***zinc, vitamin B6*** and ***vitamin B1***

It is short on ***vitamin A, folic acid, vitamin B2, vitamin E, vitamin D*** and ***vitamin B12***

We also found colouring *tartrazine* in this dish, probably in the liquor.

Our samples had surprisingly little fat (mainly in the pie) but what there was consisted of nearly 50% saturated fat. The fibre was mostly from the mash, as was the vitamin C.

Nutritionally, you should add to your diet some rich sources of the nutrients listed as insufficient. A balanced diet means plenty of fruit and vegetables and plenty of starchy foods, plus some dairy products and some lean meat and fish (or meat substitutes like beans, nuts, eggs, etc). A good balance might be achieved by adding to your diet foods rich in the missing nutrients, such as: *green and red vegetables, sweet potato, fruit, liver, tuna fish, nuts, wholegrains and wholemeal bread, vegetable oils (and sunshine for vitamin D).*

Beef chow mein

Independent take-away

The portions we looked at weighed on average 408gm, over 14oz.

Calories: 570

For the calories this food provides, it is high in ***fats*** and ***salt***

It is a good source of ***protein*** and ***vitamin C***

It gives useful amounts of ***iron, zinc, niacin, dietary fibre, calcium, vitamin A*** and ***vitamin B12***

It is short on ***folic acid, vitamin B1, vitamin B6, vitamin D, vitamin B2*** and ***vitamin E***

We found the colouring *tartrazine* in this dish, probably from the noodles. The high level of salt might be partially due to sodium found in the flavour enhancer *monosodium glutamate*, or to soya sauce which is very high in salt.

We found more vitamin C than we expected, possibly from the vegetables being used (e.g. green peppers) or from the use of canned ingredients such as bean sprouts which have added vitamin C to prevent the colours fading.

Nutritionally, you should add to your diet some rich sources of the nutrients listed as insufficient. A balanced diet means plenty of fruit and vegetables and plenty of starchy foods, plus some dairy products and some lean meat and fish (or meat substitutes like beans, nuts, eggs, etc). A good balance might be achieved by adding to your diet foods rich in the missing nutrients, such as: *green vegetables, lean meat, liver, peas, beans, wholegrains and wholemeal bread, milk, nuts, seeds (and sunshine for vitamin D).*

Cornish pasty

Bakery Chain

The portions we looked at weighed on average a total of 152gm, over 5oz.

Calories: 525

For the calories this food provides, it is high in ***fats***

It is a good source of ***vitamin B12***

It gives useful amounts of ***protein, iron, vitamin B1, dietary fibre, calcium, niacin, vitamin C, vitamin E***

It is short on ***vitamin A, zinc, vitamin D, vitamin B6, folic acid, vitamin B2***

If the pasty is made with vegetable fat then the saturated fats may not be too high, though often manufacturers will hydrogenate an unsaturated fat to make it more saturated, for ease of handling and better baking properties.

Nutritionally, you should add to your diet some rich sources of the nutrients listed as insufficient, without adding too much to the fat you eat. A balanced diet means plenty of fruit and vegetables and plenty of starchy foods, plus some dairy products and some lean meat and fish (or meat substitutes like beans, nuts, eggs, etc). A good balance might be achieved by adding to your diet foods rich in the missing nutrients, such as: *green and red vegetables, sweet potato, tuna fish, wholegrains and wholemeal bread, peas, beans, skimmed milk (and sunshine for vitamin D).*

Lamb curry

Independent take-away

The portions we looked at weighed on average a total of 314gm, nearly 11oz.

Calories: 510

For the calories this food provides, it is high in ***fats*** and ***salt***

It is a good source of ***protein, iron, zinc, niacin*** and ***vitamin B12***

It gives useful amounts of ***calcium, vitamin B2, vitamin B6, vitamin B1, vitamin E*** and ***vitamin A***

It is short on ***dietary fibre, vitamin D, vitamin C*** and ***folic acid***

There is a lot of oil in this dish, but it is mostly vegetable oil and so relatively unsaturated.

Nutritionally, you should add to your diet some rich sources of the nutrients listed as insufficient, without adding too much to the fat you eat. A balanced diet means plenty of fruit and vegetables and plenty of starchy foods, plus some dairy products and some lean meat and fish (or meat substitutes like beans, nuts, eggs, etc). A good balance might be achieved by adding to your diet foods rich in the missing nutrients, such as: *green and red vegetables, potatoes, fruit, beans and lentils (e.g. dahl), rice and wholegrains and wholemeal bread (and sunshine for vitamin D).*

Burger in a bun

Microwave self-service

The portions we looked at weighed on average a total of 210gm, nearly 7oz.

Calories: 504

For the calories this food provides, it is high in ***fats*** and ***saturated fats***

It is a good source of ***protein, iron, calcium, zinc, vitamin B12***

It gives useful amounts of ***vitamin B2, dietary fibre, niacin, vitamin B1*** and ***vitamin B6***

It is short on ***vitamin A, vitamin C, vitamin E, folic acid*** and ***vitamin D***

Burgers can differ a lot in their quality depending upon where you buy them. Some will have non-beef meats (e.g. pork) as well as added fat, colouring, flavourings and flavour enhancers such as monosodium glutamate. Others will be mostly beef, though often with added beef fat. Either way they are likely to be fairly high in fats, especially saturated fats, and will need some balancing. We found more calcium than we expected, possibly from added milk powder in the meat, or perhaps because of small fragments of bone if mechanically recovered meat had been used in the burger.

Nutritionally, you should add to your diet some rich sources of the nutrients listed as insufficient, without adding too much to the fat you eat. A balanced diet means plenty of fruit and vegetables and plenty of starchy foods, plus some dairy products and some lean meat and fish (or meat substitutes like beans, nuts, eggs, etc). A good balance might be achieved by adding to your diet foods rich in the missing nutrients, such as: *green and red vegetables, potatoes, fruit, fish, wholegrains and wholemeal bread, skimmed milk, peas, beans, nuts (and sunshine for vitamin D).*

Large shish kebab with salad

Independent take-away

The portions we looked at weighed on average a total of 370gm, around 13oz.

Calories: 485

For the calories this food provides, it is high in ***salt***

It is a good source of ***protein, calcium, iron, zinc, vitamin B1, vitamin B2*** and ***niacin***

It gives useful amounts of ***vitamin C, vitamin B12, vitamin B6*** and ***dietary fibre***

It is short on ***vitamin D, vitamin A, vitamin E*** and ***folic acid***

This is a fairly good dish for balancing your nutrients. Shish kebabs are less fatty than donor kebabs. There was only a small portion of salad with this item and a balanced meal could well do with more salad. A portion of hummus would add some of the missing nutrients.

Nutritionally, you should add to your diet some rich sources of the nutrients listed as insufficient. A balanced diet means plenty of fruit and vegetables and plenty of starchy foods, plus some dairy products and some lean meat and fish (or meat substitutes like beans, nuts, eggs, etc). A good balance might be achieved by adding to your diet foods rich in the missing nutrients, such as: *green and red vegetables, beans and lentils, nuts, seeds (and sunshine for vitamin D).*

Baked potato with vegetarian filling

Independent take-away

The portions we looked at weighed on average a total of 613gm, over 1lb 5oz.

Calories: 470

The food is a good source of ***protein, iron, calcium, vitamin B1, niacin, vitamin B6*** and ***dietary fibre***

It gives useful amounts of ***zinc, vitamin A, vitamin C, vitamin B2*** and ***folic acid***

It is short on ***vitamin B12, vitamin E*** and ***vitamin D***

This is a good all-round meal with few nutrients missing. The vegetarian filling was a spicy bean mixture. Vitamin C levels are usually good if you eat potatoes, but older potatoes will have less vitamin C than newer ones.

Nutritionally, you should add to your diet some rich sources of the nutrients listed as insufficient. A balanced diet means plenty of fruit and vegetables and plenty of starchy foods, plus some dairy products and some lean meat and fish (or meat substitutes like beans, nuts, eggs, etc). A good balance might be achieved by adding to your diet foods rich in the missing nutrients, such as: *fish, liver or cheese for the vitamin B12, vegetable oils, nuts and seeds for the vitamin E (and sunshine for vitamin D).*

Jacket potato with cheese and onion filling

Independent take-away

The portions we looked at weighed on average 281gm, around 10oz.

Calories: 460

For the calories this food provides, it is high in ***fats, saturated fats*** and ***salt***

It is a good source of ***protein, calcium*** and ***vitamin B6***

It gives useful amounts of ***iron, zinc, vitamin B1, niacin, vitamin B12, vitamin A, dietary fibre, vitamin B2*** and ***vitamin C***

It is short on ***folic acid, vitamin D*** and ***vitamin E***

The fat comes from the cheese (and butter if it is used), so another choice of filling could reduce this. But cheese is rich in calcium, so trying a low-fat cheese or dropping the cheese but drinking milk with the meal, would be lower-fat alternatives that retain the useful calcium.

Nutritionally, you should add to your diet some rich sources of the nutrients listed as insufficient. A balanced diet means plenty of fruit and vegetables and plenty of starchy foods, plus some dairy products and some lean meat and fish (or meat substitutes like beans, nuts, eggs, etc). A good balance might be achieved by adding to your diet foods rich in the missing nutrients, such as: *green vegetables, sweet potatoes, nuts, seeds (and sunshine for vitamin D).*

Steak and kidney pie

Independent take-away

The portions we looked at weighed on average 153gm, over 5oz.

Calories: 460

For the calories this food provides, it is high in ***fats*** and ***saturated fats***

It is a good source of ***protein, niacin*** and ***vitamin B12***

It gives useful amounts of ***iron, zinc, vitamin B1, vitamin A, dietary fibre*** and ***vitamin B2***

It is short on ***calcium, vitamin C, folic acid, vitamin B6, vitamin D*** and ***vitamin E***

Pies of this sort often include flavour enhancer *monosodium glutamate* and the fat in the pastry (and in the meat) may be lard. Indeed, the kidneys may be pigs' kidneys, so this dish is not for pork-avoiders. Milk powder is often used in meat pies, so this dish is not for milk-intolerance sufferers.

The kidney in this dish boosts several essential nutrients. But the meat and the pastry push the fat (and the saturated fats especially) to high levels. Eaten with chips, the dietary fibre and Vitamin C would be boosted, but so would the fat levels.

Nutritionally, you should add to your diet some rich sources of the nutrients listed as insufficient. A balanced diet means plenty of fruit and vegetables and plenty of starchy foods, plus some dairy products and some lean meat and fish (or meat substitutes like beans, nuts, eggs, etc). A good balance might be achieved by adding to your diet foods rich in the missing nutrients, such as: *green vegetables, milk, fruit, beans, wholegrains and wholemeal bread, fish, nuts, seeds (and sunshine for vitamin D).*

Jamaican patty

Independent take-away

The portions we looked at weighed on average a total of 138gm, nearly 5oz.

Calories: 455

For the calories this food provides, it is high in ***fats*** and ***saturated fats***

It is a good source of ***protein*** and ***iron***

It gives useful amounts of ***vitamin C, vitamin B1, vitamin B2, vitamin B6, zinc, calcium, vitamin B12*** and ***niacin***

It is short on ***dietary fibre, vitamin A, folic acid, vitamin E*** and ***vitamin D***

The vitamin C was presumably an added preservative.

Nutritionally, you should add to your diet some rich sources of the nutrients listed as insufficient, without adding too much to the fat you eat. A balanced diet means plenty of fruit and vegetables and plenty of starchy foods, plus some dairy products and some lean meat and fish (or meat substitutes like beans, nuts, eggs, etc). A good balance might be achieved by adding to your diet foods rich in the missing nutrients, such as: *green and red vegetables, sweet potatoes, fish, fruit, milk, wholegrains and wholemeal bread, rice, peas, nuts (and sunshine for vitamin D).*

Chicken madras

Independent take-away

The portions we looked at weighed on average a total of 339gm, around 12oz.

Calories: 430

For the calories this food provides, it is high in ***fats*** and ***salt***

It is a good source of ***protein, niacin, iron*** and ***zinc***

It gives useful amounts of ***calcium, vitamin B2, vitamin A, vitamin B6, vitamin B12*** and ***vitamin E***

It is short on ***folic acid, vitamin D, vitamin B1, vitamin C*** and ***dietary fibre***

This meal is rich in oil, but not a highly saturated one.

Nutritionally, you should add to your diet some rich sources of the nutrients listed as insufficient, while not adding too much to the fat you eat. A balanced diet means plenty of fruit and vegetables and plentyb of starchy foods, plus some dairy products and some lean meat and fish (or meat substitutes like beans, nuts, eggs, etc). A good balance might be achieved by adding to your diet foods rich in the missing ingredients, such as: *green vegetables, potatoes, beans and lentils (e.g. dahl), brown rice and whole grains, nan, chapati and wholemeal bread (and sunshine for vitamin D).*

Spring roll

Independent take-away

The portions we looked at weighed on average 193gm, nearly 7oz.

Calories: 420

For the calories this food provides, it is high in ***fats*** and ***salt***

It is a good source of ***protein***

It gives useful amounts of ***iron, dietary fibre, zinc*** and ***vitamin B12***

It is short on ***calcium, vitamin C, vitamin B1, vitamin B6, folic acid, niacin, vitamin A, vitamin B2, vitamin D*** and ***vitamin E***

Although fairly fatty, this dish is not high in saturated fat, probably because it was fried in vegetable oil. If it had higher meat content or had been fried in animal fat or a saturated vegetable fat then the amount of saturated fat would have risen. Eating chips with this meal would boost the dietary fibre and the vitamin C levels and, if fried in vegetable oil, the saturated fat levels should stay low.

Nutritionally, you should add to your diet some rich sources of the nutrients listed as insufficient, without raising the fat content too much. A balanced diet means plenty of fruit and vegetables and plenty of starchy foods, plus some dairy products and some lean meat and fish (or meat substitutes like beans, nuts, eggs, etc). A good balance might be achieved by adding to your diet foods rich in the missing nutrients, such as: *green and red vegetables, fruit, milk, lean meat, liver, fish, beans, wholegrains and wholemeal bread, milk, nuts, seeds (and sunshine for vitamin D).*

Quarterpounder

Multinational

The portions we looked at weighed on average a total of 156gm, just under 6oz.

Calories: 415

For the calories this food provides, it is high in ***fats*** and ***saturated fats***

It is a good source of ***protein, iron, zinc, niacin*** and ***vitamin B12***

It gives useful amounts of ***calcium, vitamin B6, vitamin B2*** and ***vitamin C***

It is short on ***vitamin B1, dietary fibre, vitamin A, folic acid, vitamin E*** and ***vitamin D***

Burgers are not, as many people believe, all rubbish. A good quality burger can provide some useful nutrients. Nonetheless the fat content is high and the fibre level low, so it should not be seen as a balanced meal by itself.

Nutritionally, you should add to your diet some rich sources of the nutrients listed as insufficient, without adding too much to the fat you eat. A balanced diet means plenty of fruit and vegetables and plenty of starchy foods, plus some dairy products and some lean meat and fish (or meat substitutes like beans, nuts, eggs, etc). A good balance might be achieved by adding to your diet foods rich in the missing nutrients, such as: *green and red vegetables, potatoes, fruit, wholegrains and wholemeal bread, peas, beans, nuts (and sunshine for vitamin D).*

Sausage in batter

Independent take-away

The portions we looked at weighed on average 166gm, just under 6oz.

Calories: 410

For the calories this food provides, it is high in ***fats, saturated fats*** and ***salt***

It is a good source of ***protein, calcium, niacin*** and ***vitamin B12***

It gives useful amounts of ***iron, vitamin C*** and ***zinc***

It is short on ***dietary fibre, vitamin E, folic acid, vitamin B1, vitamin A, vitamin B2, vitamin D*** and ***vitamin B6***

We found the colourings *tartrazine*, *ponceau 4R* and *red 2G* in this meal, the former probably coming from the batter and the latter from the sausage. The ponceau could have been in either.

We found more calcium than we expected, which could come from added milk products in the sausage or from the use of mechanically recovered meat (with fine bone particles) used as part of the sausage meat. We also found more vitamin C then we expected, probably from being added to the sausage as an antioxidant to prevent the fat from going rancid and the colouring from fading during long storage times.

It is unlikely that this dish would be eaten on its own. Having a portion of chips would boost the dietary fibre and the vitamin C, although the total fat levels would then get rather high.

Nutritionally, you should add to your diet some rich sources of the nutrients listed as insufficient, while not adding too much to the overall calories you eat. A balanced diet means plenty of fruit and vegetables and plenty of starchy foods, plus some dairy products and some lean meat and fish (or meat substitutes like beans, nuts, eggs, etc). A good balance might be achieved by adding to your diet foods rich in the missing nutrients, such as: *green and red vegetables, sweet potato, fruit, lean red meat, liver, fish, wholegrains and wholemeal bread, skimmed milk, nuts, peas, beans, lentils (and sunshine for vitamin D).*

Deep fried chicken

Independent take-away

The portions we looked at weighed on average 149gm, over 5oz.

Calories: 390

For the calories this food provides, it is high in ***fats*** and ***salt***

It is a good source of ***protein, niacin*** and ***vitamin B6***

It gives useful amounts of ***iron, vitamin B1, zinc*** and ***vitamin B2***

It is short on ***calcium, vitamin C, folic acid, dietary fibre, vitamin A, vitamin D, vitamin E*** and ***vitamin B12***

If the deep fried chicken is un-coated then it is unlikely to have many additives, except possibly sodium polyphosphate which helps retain water. But if the chicken is coated in a savoury crumb (probably applied by dipping in batter mix and then in crumb mix) then this coating may have *monosodium glutamate* and colouring agents such as *tartrazine* or *annatto*.

Nutritionally, you should add to your diet some rich sources of the nutrients listed as insufficient, while not adding too much to the fat you eat. A balanced diet means plenty of fruit and vegetables and plenty of starchy foods, plus some dairy products and some lean meat and fish (or meat substitutes like beans, nuts, eggs, etc). A good balance might be achieved by adding to your diet foods rich in the missing nutrients, such as: *green and red vegetables, potatoes, liver, skimmed milk, fruit, beans, wholegrains and wholemeal bread, nuts, seeds (and sunshine for vitamin D).*

Pilau rice

Independent take-away

The portions we looked at weighed on average a total of 241gm, over 8oz.

Calories: 390

The food gives useful amounts of ***dietary fibre, zinc*** and ***protein***

It is short on ***iron, vitamin C, vitamin B2, vitamin D, vitamin B1, vitamin A, folic acid, vitamin B6, vitamin B12, vitamin E, calcium*** and ***niacin***

The dish consisted of rice which had been artificially coloured. We found *sunset yellow* and *ponceau* in our samples.

On its own this dish provided little more than a large serving of starch and water. Starchy foods are useful but they need to be accompanied by foods rich in nutrients.

Nutritionally, you should add to your diet some rich sources of the nutrients listed as insufficient. A balanced diet means plenty of fruit and vegetables and plenty of starchy foods, plus some dairy products and some lean meat and fish (or meat substitutes like beans, nuts, eggs, etc). A good balance might be achieved by adding to your diet foods rich in the missing nutrients, such as: *green and red vegetables, fruit, milk, eggs, liver, lean meats, oily fish, e.g. tuna fish, sweet potato, wholegrains and wholemeal bread, nuts, seeds (and sunshine for vitamin D).*

Large frankfurter

Microwave self-service

The portions we looked at weighed on average a total of 188gm, nearly 7oz.

Calories: 375

For the calories this food provides, it is high in ***salt***

It is a good source of ***protein, iron*** and ***vitamin B12***

It gives useful amounts of ***calcium, vitamin B1, zinc, niacin, vitamin B2*** and ***dietary fibre***

It is short on ***vitamin A, folic acid, vitamin C, vitamin B6, vitamin D*** and ***vitamin E***

We found that this item had been coloured with "nature-identical" colours, i.e. added colouring which mimic colourings that can be found in nature (though not in meat like frankfurter meat). Although they are similar to chemicals found in nature, nature-identical colours are usually synthetic, and their original counterparts in nature may not be in food at all but in insects, tree bark, feathers, shells or burnt plants.

The levels of dietary fibre were higher than expected, possibly due to the added thickeners and bulking agents used in the meat. The calcium levels may also have been boosted by small fragments of bone if mechanically recovered meat had been used in this product or milk powder added.

Nutritionally, you should add to your diet some rich sources of the nutrients listed as insufficient. A balanced diet means plenty of fruit and vegetables and plenty of starchy foods, plus some dairy products and some lean meat and fish (or meat substitutes like beans, nuts, eggs, etc). A good balance might be achieved by adding to your diet foods rich in the missing nutrients, such as: *green and red vegetables, potatoes, eggs, nuts, peas, beans, tuna fish, wholegrains and wholemeal bread, skimmed milk (and sunshine for vitamin D).*

Cheese and onion pasty

Bakery chain

The portions we looked at weighed on average a total of 100gm, just over 4oz.

Calories: 360

For the calories this food provides, it is high in ***fats*** and ***saturated fats***

It is a good source of ***calcium***

It gives useful amounts of ***protein, niacin, vitamin C, dietary fibre, vitamin A, vitamin B2, vitamin B12*** and ***vitamin E***

It is short on ***iron, zinc, vitamin D, vitamin B6, folic acid*** and *vitamin B1*

This pasty is high in fat especially saturated fat. Commercial pastry mix usually includes lard or a hydrogenated vegetable fat, both of them high in saturates. It is partly redeemed by the potatoes which contribute some useful vitamin C (which may also be present as an added antioxidant) and some dietary fibre.

Nutritionally, you should add to your diet some rich sources of the nutrients listed as insufficient, without adding too much to the fat you eat. A balanced diet means plenty of fruit and vegetables and plenty of starchy foods, plus some dairy products and some lean meat and fish (or meat substitutes like beans, nuts, eggs, etc). A good balance might be achieved by adding to your diet foods rich in the missing nutrients, such as: *green vegetables, lean meat, liver, wholegrains and wholemeal bread, peas, beans (and sunshine for vitamin D).*

Onion bhaji

Independent take-away

The portions we looked at weighed on average 118gm, just over 4oz.

Calories: 355

For the calories this food provides, it is high in ***fats***

It is a good source of ***protein*** and ***iron***

It gives useful amounts of ***calcium, zinc, niacin, vitamin E*** and ***dietary fibre***

It is short on ***vitamin C, vitamin B1, vitamin B6, folic acid, vitamin D, vitamin B2, vitamin B12*** and ***vitamin A***

The yellow colour of the bhajis is artificial. We found both *tartrazine* and *sunset yellow* dyes in our samples.

The fat levels are fairly high in this dish because the bhajis are fried in fat and retain much of that fat when they are served. Usually the fat is a relatively unsaturated vegetable oil, but might be a more saturated ghee.

Nutritionally, you should add to your diet some rich sources of the nutrients listed as insufficient without adding to the fat. A balanced diet means plenty of fruit and vegetables and plenty of starchy foods, plus some dairy products and some lean meat and fish (or meat substitutes like beans, nuts, eggs, etc). A good balance might be achieved by adding to your diet foods rich in the missing nutrients, such as: *green and red vegetables, potatoes, lean meat, liver, eggs, skimmed milk, fruit, beans and lentils, wholegrains and wholemeal bread (and sunshine for vitamin D).*

Beef salad roll

Independent take-away

The portions we looked at weighed on average 185gm, under 7oz.

Calories: 350

The food is a good source of ***protein, niacin*** and ***vitamin B12***

It gives useful amounts of ***iron, calcium, dietary fibre, vitamin B6, zinc, vitamin A*** and ***vitamin B2***

It is short on ***vitamin B1, folic acid, vitamin E, vitamin C*** and ***vitamin D***

This is a less fatty alternative to deep fried fast foods. What fat there is, though, tends to be saturated (from the beef, and possibly from the butter or caterer's hard margarine). Some cold beef used for catering has added *polyphosphates* (to hold water in the meat), added milk products (casein and lactose) and added flavour enhancer (*monosodium glutamate*). The salad portions can be very useful if they are generous and overall this is one of the better take-away foods.

Nutritionally, you should add to your diet some rich sources of the nutrients listed as insufficient. A balanced diet means plenty of fruit and vegetables and plenty of starchy foods, plus some dairy products and some lean meat and fish (or meat substitutes like beans, nuts, eggs, etc). A good balance might be achieved by adding to your diet foods rich in the missing nutrients, such as: *green vegetables, sweet potato, fruit, fish, wholegrains and wholemeal bread, milk, nuts, beans, vegetable oils (and sunshine for vitamin D).*

Cheese Salad Roll

Independent take-away

The portions we looked at weighed on average 171gm, just over 6oz.

Calories: 345

For the calories this food provides, it is high in ***salt***

It is a good source of ***protein, calcium*** and ***vitamin A***

It gives useful amounts of ***zinc, vitamin B2, vitamin B12, dietary fibre*** and ***niacin***

It is short on ***iron, folic acid, vitamin B1, vitamin E, vitamin C, vitamin D*** and ***vitamin B6***

This is a less fatty alternative to deep fried fast foods. What fat there is, though, tends to be saturated (from the cheese and possibly from the butter or caterer's hard margarine). The salad portions can be very useful if they are generous.

Nutritionally, you should add to your diet some rich sources of the nutrients listed as insufficient. A balanced diet means plenty of fruit and vegetables and plenty of starchy foods, plus some dairy products and some lean meat and fish (or meat substitutes like beans, nuts, eggs, etc). A good balance might be achieved by adding to your diet foods rich in the missing nutrients, such as: *green vegetables, potatoes and sweet potato, fruit, fish, wholegrains and wholemeal bread, nuts, peas, beans vegetable oils, (and sunshine for vitamin D).*

Cheese and tomato sandwich (white)

Bakery chain

The portions we looked at weighed on average a total of 145gm, just over 5oz.

Calories: 335

The food is a good source of ***protein, calcium*** and ***vitamin A***

It gives useful amounts of ***vitamin B12*** and ***niacin***

It is short on ***vitamin B1, iron, vitamin C, vitamin D, dietary fibre, zinc, folic acid, vitamin B6, vitamin E*** and ***vitamin B2***

The small amount of fat provided is rather rich in saturated fats (from the cheese and the butter or hard margarine). The tomato is barely a gesture towards some vegetables so vegetables or fruit are certainly needed to balance this meal. Choosing cream cheese rather than cheddar could make matters worse as cream cheese has less calcium and niacin. Cottage cheese, although lower in calories and fats, is low in calcium, niacin and vitamin A. However, cottage cheese eaten with wholemeal bread and some raw vegetables or fruit would be a good balance.

Nutritionally, you should add to your diet some rich sources of the nutrients listed as insufficient. A balanced diet means plenty of fruit and vegetables and plenty of starchy foods, plus some dairy products and some lean meat and fish (or meat substitutes like beans, nuts, eggs, etc). A good balance might be achieved by adding to your diet foods rich in the missing nutrients, such as: *green vegetables, fruit, lean meat, tuna fish, wholegrains and wholemeal bread, nuts, seeds (and sunshine for vitamin D).*

Cheese and cucumber sandwich (brown)

Bakery chain

The portions we looked at weighed on average a total of 140gm, just under 5oz.

Calories: 330

The food is a good source of ***protein, calcium, vitamin A*** and ***niacin***

It gives useful amounts of ***vitamin B1, vitamin B2, dietary fibre, zinc*** and ***vitamin B12***

It is short on ***iron, vitamin C, vitamin D, folic acid, vitamin B6*** and ***vitamin E***

What fat there is here is rather rich in saturated fats (from the cheese and the butter or hard margarine). The cucumber is barely a gesture towards some vegetables so vegetables or fruit are certainly needed to balance this meal. The brown bread is not usually wholemeal and may just be a white bread coloured with a caramel agent made of glucose and caustic soda or ammonia.

Nutritionally, you should add to your diet some rich sources of the nutrients listed as insufficient. A balanced diet means plenty of fruit and vegetables and plenty of starchy foods, plus some dairy products and some lean meat and fish (or meat substitutes like beans, nuts, eggs, etc). A good balance might be achieved by adding to your diet foods rich in the missing nutrients, such as: *green and red vegetables, fruit, tuna fish, wholegrains and wholemeal bread, nuts, seeds (and sunshine for vitamin D).*

Sausage roll

Bakery chain

The portions we looked at weighed on average a total of 75gm, under 3oz.

Calories: 295

For the calories this food provides, it is high in ***fats***

It is a good source of ***calcium***

It gives useful amounts of ***protein, vitamin D, dietary fibre, niacin, vitamin C*** and ***vitamin E***

It is short on ***vitamin A, iron, vitamin B1, vitamin B2, vitamin B6, zinc, folic acid*** and ***vitamin B12***

We found the artificial colouring *red 2G* in this meal, probably from the sausage-meat.

Unexpectedly, calcium levels were high. This will be partly from the pastry and perhaps also from the added thickeners and bulking agents. But it could also have come either from unintended ground bone, if the meat included mechanically recovered meat, or from added skimmed milk powder. Dietary fibre levels were unusually high, probably from the added thickeners and bulking agents in the sausage-meat. Vitamin C levels were also high, probably because it had been added as a preservative and antioxidant. The level of vitamin B1 might have been higher if the meat were lean pork.

Generally, this item was a poor source of nutrients, although it was partly redeemed by the unexpectedly high levels of calcium and vitamin C.

Nutritionally, you should add to your diet some rich sources of the nutrients listed as insufficient. A balanced diet means plenty of fruit and vegetables and plenty of starchy foods, plus some dairy products and some lean meat and fish (or meat substitutes like beans, nuts, eggs, etc). A good balance might be achieved by adding to your diet foods rich in the missing nutrients, such as: *green and red vegetables, lean meat, liver, nuts, tuna fish, wholegrains and wholemeal bread, skimmed milk (and sunshine for vitamin D).*

Fried egg roll

Independent take-away

The portions we looked at weighed on average a total of 104gm, just under 4oz.

Calories: 275

The food is a good source of ***protein, iron*** and ***vitamin B12***

It gives useful amounts of ***calcium, zinc, vitamin B1, dietary fibre, vitamin A, niacin, vitamin B2, vitamin C, vitamin E*** and ***vitamin D***

It is short on ***vitamin B6*** and ***folic acid***

This is a better balanced dish than one might expect, partly because eggs are a rich source of many nutrients. The vitamin C levels are higher than expected, possibly because vitamin C was added as a preservative in the bread roll. The amount of dietary fibre would depend on the sort of flour used in the bread roll.

To be sure of sufficient vitamin C and dietary fibre, you could add some potatoes, perhaps even chips if they are fried in good vegetable oil.

Nutritionally, you should add to your diet some rich sources of the nutrients listed as insufficient. A balanced diet means plenty of fruit and vegetables and plenty of starchy foods, plus some dairy products and some lean meat and fish (or meat substitutes like beans, nuts, eggs, etc). A good balance might be achieved by adding to your diet foods rich in the missing nutrients, such as: *green vegetables, potatoes, fish.*

Apple pie

Multinational

The portions we looked at weighed on average a total of 86gm, about 3oz.

Calories: 250

For the calories this food provides, it is high in ***fats*** and ***saturated fat***

It gives useful amounts of ***calcium*** and ***vitamin C***

It is short on ***protein, niacin, vitamin A, vitamin D, vitamin B1, dietary fibre, folic acid, iron, zinc, vitamin B6, vitamin B2, vitamin B12*** and ***vitamin E***

The saturated fats here may be partly a result of deep frying in animal fats, such as beef tallow. Frying in a non-hydrogenated vegetable oil would help improve this dish a little. But generally it provides very poor nutrition and should not be relied on for a regular meal.

Nutritionally, you should add to your diet some rich sources of the nutrients listed as insufficient, without adding too much to the fat you eat. A balanced diet means plenty of fruit and vegetables and plenty of starchy foods, plus some dairy products and some lean meat and fish (or meat substitutes like beans, nuts, eggs, etc). A good balance might be achieved by adding to your diet foods rich in the missing nutrients, such as: *green and red vegetables, sweet potato, fruit, lean red meat, tuna fish, wholegrains and wholemeal bread, peas, beans and lentils, skimmed milk (and sunshine for vitamin D).*

Fried bacon roll
Independent take-away

The portions we looked at weighed on average a total of 79gm, just under 3oz.

Calories: 245

For the calories this food provides, it is high in ***salt***

It is a good source of ***protein, iron*** and ***vitamin B1***

It gives useful amounts of ***zinc, vitamin B6, niacin, vitamin B2, vitamin C*** and ***dietary fibre***

It is short on ***calcium, vitamin B12, vitamin A, folic acid, vitamin E*** and ***vitamin D***

As with the previous item, the dietary fibre levels will depend on the sort of flour used in the bread roll, while the vitamin C levels (which were higher here than expected) may reflect the use of vitamin C as an added preservative in the bread.

To be sure of getting vitamin C and dietary fibre, add some potatoes to this dish, perhaps even chips if fried in good vegetable oil. If the bacon were grilled then some of its fat, which is highly saturated, would be lost. Most bacon still includes the preserving and curing agent *sodium nitrate* which has been suspected of being linked to stomach cancer.

Nutritionally, you should add to your diet some rich sources of the nutrients listed as insufficient. A balanced diet means plenty of fruit and vegetables and plenty of starchy foods, plus some dairy products and some lean meat and fish (or meat substitutes like beans, nuts, eggs, etc). A good balance might be achieved by adding to your diet foods rich in the missing nutrients, such as: *green and red vegetables, potatoes, milk, peas, nuts (and sunshine for vitamin D).*

Fish cake

Independent take-away

The portions we looked at weighed on average 78gm, nearly 3oz.

Calories: 200

For the calories this food provides, it is high in ***fats***

It is a good source of ***protein*** and ***niacin***

It gives useful amounts of ***calcium, vitamin B12, vitamin B6, dietary fibre*** and ***vitamin C***

It is short on ***iron, vitamin A, folic acid, vitamin B1, zinc, vitamin B2, vitamin D*** and ***vitamin E***

It is unlikely you would eat a fish cake alone, and having some chips would boost the dietary fibre and the vitamin C levels.

Nutritionally, you should add to your diet some rich sources of the nutrients listed as insufficient. A balanced diet means plenty of fruit and vegetables and plenty of starchy foods, plus some dairy products and some lean meat and fish (or meat substitutes like beans, nuts, eggs, etc). A good balance might be achieved by adding to your diet foods rich in the missing nutrients, such as: *green and red vegetables, sweet potato, fruit, lean red meat, milk, eggs, wholegrains and wholemeal bread, vegetable oils, nuts (and sunshine for vitamin D).*

Large cola

Multinational

The portions we looked at weighed on average a total of 549gm, measuring nearly a pint.

Calories: 200

For the calories this food provides, it is high in ***sugar***

It is short on ***protein, vitamin A, vitamin D, dietary fibre, iron, vitamin B1, vitamin B2, calcium, niacin, vitamin B6, vitamin C, vitamin E, zinc, folic acid*** and ***vitamin B12***

This drink is coloured with chemically derived caramel colourant and contains a neural stimulant, caffeine.

The large cola tested had over 55gm of sugar in it, more than 12 spoonfuls of sugar. Apart from these empty calories it was nutritionally of little value.

Nutritionally, you should add to your diet some rich sources of the nutrients listed as insufficient. A balanced diet means plenty of fruit and vegetables and plenty of starchy foods, plus some dairy products and some lean meat and fish (or meat substitutes like beans, nuts, eggs, etc). To balance a drink like this you need to ensure you add to your diet some rich sources of the nutrients listed as insufficient, without adding too much to the calories you eat – i.e. nourishing food of any sort.

French fries

Multinational

The portions we looked at weighed on average a total of 58gm, just over 2oz.

Calories: 175

For the calories this food provides, it is high in ***fats*** and ***saturated fats***

It is a good source of ***protein*** and ***vitamin C***

It gives useful amounts of ***dietary fibre, vitamin B6*** and ***vitamin E***

It is short on ***protein, calcium, zinc, vitamin A, vitamin B12, vitamin B1, iron, niacin, vitamin B2, vitamin D*** and ***folic acid***

The vitamin E levels would depend on the type of oil being used, as would the saturated fat levels. In this case the fat seems to have been animal fat - probably beef tallow - with the result that saturated fat levels are high and vitamin E levels low.

The potatoes provide useful vitamin C and dietary fibre, although the small portions we were served would make little impact on an adult's daily needs.

Nutritionally, you should add to your diet some rich sources of the nutrients listed as insufficient. A balanced diet means plenty of fruit and vegetables and plenty of starchy foods, plus some dairy products and some lean meat and fish (or meat substitutes like beans, nuts, eggs, etc). A good balance might be achieved by adding to your diet foods rich in the missing nutrients, such as: *green and red vegetables, milk, wholegrains and wholemeal bread, beans and lentils, liver, lean meat, fish, nuts, seeds (and sunshine for vitamin D).*

Cod roe in batter

Independent take-away

The portions we looked at weighed on average 94gm, over 3oz.

Calories: 160

For the calories this food provides, it is high in ***fats*** and ***salt***

It is a good source of ***protein, vitamin A, vitamin D, vitamin E, vitamin B1, vitamin B2, niacin*** and ***vitamin B12***

It gives useful amounts of ***iron, zinc, vitamin B6, calcium*** and ***vitamin C***

It is short on ***dietary fibre*** and ***folic acid***

We found the colourings *tartrazine* and *ponceau 4R* in this dish, the tartrazine almost certainly coming from the batter mix being used and the ponceau in either the batter or the roe.

It is unlikely that this dish would be eaten on its own and

having chips with it would boost the dietary fibre and vitamin C levels. The fat in cod roe is not too high in saturates and indeed contains some essential fatty acids in useful quantities. This is certainly one of the better fast food items we looked at.

Nutritionally, you should add to your diet some rich sources of the nutrients listed as insufficient. A balanced diet means plenty of fruit and vegetables and plenty of starchy foods, plus some dairy products and some lean meat and fish (or meat substitutes like beans, nuts, eggs, etc). A good balance might be achieved by adding to your diet foods rich in the missing nutrients, such as: *green vegetables, nuts, seeds.*

Milk shakes: banana, chocolate and strawberry
Independent and multinational

The portions we looked at weighed on average a total of 135 to 155gm (small) or 275gm (large). The added air made them fill cartons of around half a pint (small) and a pint (large).

Calories: 95 to 115 (small), 290 (large)

For the calories this food provides, it is high in ***sugar***

It is a good source of ***protein*** and ***calcium***

It gives useful amounts of ***vitamin B2, vitamin A*** and ***vitamin B12***

It is short on ***dietary fibre, vitamin D, niacin, iron, vitamin B1, vitamin E, vitamin C, vitamin B6, zinc*** and ***folic acid***

Various additives are used to make the milk froth up and hold its air and to colour and flavour the drink. These can include chemicals derived from seaweed, wood pulp or cotton by-products and unidentified flavouring agents synthesised in laboratories.

No one expects milk shake to offer a balanced meal. But it is nutritionally worse than plain milk for a number of reasons: it has lost some of its vitamin C; it will have added thickeners, emulsifiers, stabilising agents, sequestrants, flavourings and colourings; and it will have large amounts of added sugar – we found nearly eight spoonfuls of sugar in the large size shake.

Some companies add skimmed milk powder to their shake mix which gives it extra nutrient richness, especially calcium and to some extent zinc and niacin, without adding to the fat levels. Otherwise the fat was similar to the levels found in fresh milk and was nearly two-thirds saturated fat.

Nutritionally, you should add to your diet some rich sources of the nutrients listed as insufficient. A balanced diet means plenty of fruit and vegetables and plenty of starchy foods, plus some dairy products and some lean meat and fish (or meat substitutes like beans, nuts, eggs, etc). A good balance might be achieved by adding to your diet foods rich in the missing nutrients, such as: *green vegetables, potatoes, lean meat, peas, beans, nuts, tuna fish, wholegrains and wholemeal bread (and sunshine for vitamin D).*

A fast look at fast foods

In summary, here is a very fast look at our fast food menu items:

Item	Good points	Bad points	Needed to balance	Note:
Fish and chips	Protein, calcium, vitamins B6, B12	High fat: many other vitamins low	Fresh veg and fruit, lean meat, wholegrains	Tartrazine in batter
Fried chicken and chips	Protein, vitamins B3, B6	High fat; many other vitamins low	Fruit and vegetables, fish, wholegrains	Monosodium glutamate in coating
Doner kebab with salad	Protein, zinc, some vitamins	High fat; a few vitamins low	More salad, fruit and wholegrains, pulses	Meat fatty, other-wise good
Shish kebab with salad	Protein, calcium, iron, zinc, some vitamins	A few vitamins low	Vegetables, pulses	Good. Try with hummus & extra salad
Sweet & Sour chicken and egg fried rice	Protein, iron, calcium	High fat; a few vitamins low	Fruit and veg, lean meat, nuts, skimmed milk	Tartrazine
Cheese & tomato pizza	Protein, calcium, some vitamins	One or two vitamins low	Green vege-tables, fish	One of the better dishes
Beefburger in bun	Protein, iron, vitamin B12	High fat; low in several vitamins	Fruit and veg, fish, potato, pulses, milk, wholegrains	O.K. now and then
Cheeseburger and fries	Protein, calcium some vitamins	High fat; low in several vitamins	Fruit and vege-tables, fish, wholegrains, milk	May have azo dyes
Cod roe in batter	Protein, many vitamins	Low fibre	Potatoes, green vegetables	May have azo dyes, but good dish to eat
Sausage in batter	Protein, calcium, vitamins B3, B12	High fat; low fibre; many vitamins low	Fruit and veg, fish, wholegrains, milk	May have azo dyes
Spare ribs in sauce	Protein, calcium, zinc, some vitamins	Low iron, some vitamins low	Fruit and veg, pulses, lean meat, wholegrains	May have azo dyes & mono-sodium glut.

Spring roll	Protein	High fat; low calcium and many vitamins	Fruit and veg, milk, fish, lean meat, pulses, wholegrains	Poor on its own
Chicken madras	Protein, iron, zinc	High fat; low fibre and some vitamins	Fruit and veg, pulses, whole-grains	O.K. if with dahl or potato
Lamb Curry	Protein, iron, zinc, some vitamins	High fat; low fibre and some vitamins	Potatoes, fruit, pulses, green veg, wholegrains	O.K. if with dahl or potato
Cheese & onion pasty	Calcium	High fat; low in iron, zinc & some vitamins	Fruit, veg, lean meat, fish, milk, wholegrains, pulses	Not brilliant on its own
Deep-fried apple pie		High fat; poor on many other nutrients	Full range of nutritious foods	Poor on its own
French fries	Vitamin C	High fat; poor on many other nutrients	Full range of nutritious foods	Poor on its own
Milk shake	Protein, calcium	High sugar; low fibre and several nutrients	Fruit and veg, potato, lean meat, pulses, fish, wholegrains	Poor on its own

Chapter 5 **Fast food and ill-health**

We have shown how difficult it can be to have a healthy diet if it is based on fast foods. The British diet has long been regarded as among the worst in the industrialised world. The fast food revolution appears to have done nothing to improve this poor reputation and may have made it even worse.

Firstly, the range of items available from a fast food menu is small and so the choice and opportunity to make a balanced meal from the range on offer is limited. (They keep the range small in order to make it easy to serve the food fast.) Some major chains, including McDonald's, are now offering salad bars alongside the hot, fast-service counter, *although not in the UK*. In Europe, yes. In the USA, yes. But not here.

In any event, salad bars are not the complete answer to healthy eating, especially if the salads are laden with high calorie sauces. But at least they broaden the range of foods available. As it is, even if you are well-informed you are unlikely to be able to get a good balance of nutrients from any single fast food restaurant.

Secondly, you cannot easily get the information you need to be "well-informed" about your fast food meal. The fast food companies are under no obligation to tell you what is in their products: not the ingredients, not the recipes, not the composition of the food, not the nutritional content. Under present regulations they are under no obligation to tell you any of these facts. What some of the larger companies are now beginning to tell you about their products, in glossy leaflets, may not be exactly what you need to know anyway (we shall look at these leaflets more closely later). Without the information we give in this book you would be left guessing, which is not the best way of ensuring you can get what you need.

Thirdly, fast foods may contain ingredients which you wouldn't or shouldn't eat. Perhaps all the salt or monosodium glutamate, the colouring and the "tasty" coatings and crumbs and batters are actually hiding inferior products which have less nutritional value than you should expect. Manufacturers don't have to tell you and you have no legal right to know. But you can be suspicious! As we have shown in the earlier parts of this book and in the ingredients listings at the back, you may have good grounds for these suspicions.

Fourthly, much of the food served up as a fast meal will be at the most highly processed end of the range of foods available in the high street. It is also likely to be the most over-cooked. Many chips, for example, are already cooked or par-fried before being re-cooked in the deep fryer for quick serving. Pies and pasties will be cooked and stored and then heated and warm-held before being sold. Take-away meals may well be ready cooked, canned and re-heated for serving, or else cooked a long time in advance and kept ready for microwaving before being sold. All this can lead to a reduction in the nutritional value of the food. If the re-heating or second cooking processes are not done properly, you could end up with a "runny tummy" as well.

All these factors have a bearing on how fast foods can jeopardise our ability to look after our health. The content of the food, the lack of information, the methods and processes used to produce and serve the food can all have a bearing on the value of fast foods from a health angle. Fast foods may have an exaggerated reputation for being junk foods. But the fact is fast foods do tend to rate low on nutrients and high on calories. They reflect the general tendency for foods to lose their nutritional value as they are processed from their primary, raw ingredients into their more refined, mass produced forms. Fast foods are at the frontier of food technology and so demonstrate all that is best and all that is worst about the industrialisation of our food supply.

Cheap calories

The energy we extract from our food is measured in calories. The energy is produced when fat, carbohydrate and protein is "burnt up" almost literally with the oxygen we breathe, in our muscles and other body tissues.

All plants and animals used for food also provide varying amounts of vitamins and minerals as well as calories. Plants also provide dietary fibre. However, the new wonders of modern food technology have given manufacturers the ability to separate these components of food and, with an amazing array of chemical and mechanical processes, dress up these separate components to look like food again.

What this means in practice is that we are offered the calories without the rest of the original food they were

Table 5.1 **Price of a thousand Calories in various foods**

	£.p per 1000 Calories
Beef stewing steak	1.70p
Beef sausages	.70p
Beef fat (suet)	.15p
Pork chops	1.10p
Pork luncheon meat	.65p
Pork fat (lard)	.12p
Whole wheat	.14p
White flour	.09p
Soya beans	.20p
Soya oil	.06p

source: LFC data

extracted from. We are sold sugar extracted from cane or beet, starch extracted from wheat or maize, pork fat cut from the lean and refined into lard. The food refining industries dominate our diets with cheap processed calories. But the problem for us is that by stripping the calories from their original foods, the processors leave behind some valuable parts we also need – the fibre, vitamins and minerals that are found in, for example, sugar cane, sugar beet, wheat, maize and lean meat.

As Table 5.1 shows, these mass manufactured calories are cheap to produce and cheaper to buy than their original, more nutritious forms.

Any food might lose some nutritional value when it is cooked or processed, but many products are further "diluted" by the addition of cheaper ingredients to make up the recipe. As we showed in the industrial burger and sausage recipes in Chapter Two, meat products often have animal fat added to the lean meat. Indeed, Britain is one of the few countries of the world actually to *import* pig fat from the countries of Europe to the tune of 15,000 tons annually, for the manufacturers to add to your pies and pasties, sausages and burgers. Manufacturers also use polyphosphate salts to hold extra water. They use flour, bread, rusk and sugar to bulk out the meat. They replace the meat

Table 5.2 **Fast foods - calories up and nutrient richness down**

	Calories in a 100g serving	*Key nutrients in each 100 Calories*		
Beef (lean)	123	16g protein	1.7mg iron	200ug vitamin B2
Beef burger meat	264	6g protein	0.9mg iron	80ug vitamin B2
Steak & kidney pie	323	1g protein	0.8mg iron	46ug vitamin B2
Pork chops (lean)	226	14g protein		390ug vitamin B1
Saveloy	262	4g protein		50ug vitamin B1
Sausage roll	479	2g protein		23ug vitamin B1
Fish (cod)	76	23g protein		430ug vitamin B6
Cod fried in batter	199	10g protein		150ug vitamin B6
Fried fish fingers	233	6g protein		90ug vitamin B6
Potatoes	87	2.4g fibre		8-20mg vitamin C
Chips (average)	253	1.0g fibre		2-6mg vitamin C
French fries (McDonald)	311	(1.0g fibre)*		1-2mg vitamin C
Milk	65	5g protein		185mg calcium
Shake (Burger King)	115	3g protein		93mg calcium
Orange juice	38			130mg vitamin C
Orange juice (McDonald)	51			57mg vitamin C
Orange drink (McDonald)	33			0mg vitamin C

source: company data and LFC data/McCance
* no comparable fibre figure for McDonald french fries

protein with cheaper proteins from milk powder and soya flour.

These cheaper ingredients are all too often lower in nutrients but higher in calories (and higher in profits) than the food they are replacing. (Sometimes, though, they may be low in calories, but just as high in profits, such as the added water in chicken or whipped up air in milk shakes.) In many cases the end result is a product with more calories than they started with and fewer of the nutrients you would expect. Table 5.2 shows the increased calories and/or decreased nutrients for several typical fast foods when compared with their basic original ingredient. The nutrients selected are those for which the original ingredient is considered a rich and valuable source.

Looking at the tables of figures may not be the easiest way to absorb the points we are trying to make in this book. Here is another way of looking at fast foods, comparing the sort of meal you might buy in a burger bar with a meal prepared at home which supplies a similar amount of energy. The home-prepared meal was cheaper to buy but needed fuel and time to prepare it.

Table 5.3 **A fast food meal and a home cooked meal compared**

	Burger, fries & cola	*Home-made hot pot, fruit yoghurt, apple*
Cost:	£2.00–£2.50p	under £1.50p
Calories:	630–700	640
Fat:	23g	19g
Dietary fibre:	5g	6g
Protein:	16g	42g
Iron:	1mg	5mg
Calcium:	70-80mg	260mg
Vitamin A:	10ug	1200ug
Vitamin C:	4mg	27mg
Vitamin B1:	0.2mg	0.3mg
Vitamin B2:	0.2mg	0.7mg
Niacin:	5mg	20mg
Vitamin B6:	0.4mg	0.9mg
Vitamin B12:	0.5ug	4.0ug
Folate:	35ug	44ug
Vitamin E:	0.5mg	1.1mg

source: industry data and LFC/McCance

Nutrients: a British gallery of shame

There is good evidence to suggest that people in Britain suffer a whole range of diet-related disease, from heart disease and cancer through to iron deficiency, tooth decay and diabetes.

Some groups of people in particular have been found to be suffering from a shortfall in specific vitamins and minerals:

- A survey of 231 children in 112 households in a poor area of London in the mid-1970s found that a quarter of the children were getting low levels of iron and vitamin D[5/1]
- A study of 375 adolescents found their diets to be low in calcium[5/2]
- Two studies in Glasgow found that children were getting low levels of iron and vitamin D and one study also found they were getting low levels of calcium[5/3]
- Government food consumption figures show that larger families on low incomes tend to be getting insufficient iron in their household food. Half of all such families are getting less than 85% of their recommended needs[5/4]
- A survey of women aged 15 to 25 in low-income households found that the majority of them were getting less than 70% of their recommended iron needs. Folic acid intake was also very low, and vitamin B1 and vitamin B2 levels were below the levels recommended[5/5]
- A study of pregnant women from low-income households, attending a Salvation Army hospital in London's East End, found:

  47% getting below recommended levels of vitamin B1

  50% getting below recommended levels of vitamin B2

  71% getting below recommended levels of folic acid

  88% getting below recommended levels of vitamin B6

  55% getting below recommended levels of vitamin C

  41% getting below recommended levels of vitamin A

  95% getting below recommended levels of vitamin D

  The study found that women with insufficient vitamins in their diet were more likely to give birth to low-weight babies[5/6]
- Lastly, a study of British school children found:

  a third of the boys and half the girls were getting less than the recommended levels of *calcium* two-thirds of the boys and 90% of the girls were getting less than the recommended levels of *iron*

a fifth of the boys and a quarter of the girls were getting less than the recommended levels of *vitamin B1*

over 25% of the older boys and over 60% of the older girls were getting less than the recommended levels of *vitamin B2*

virtually all the children were falling short of the recommended levels of *vitamin B6*

nearly 40% of all children were getting less than the recommended levels of *vitamin A*

up to a fifth of all children were getting less than the recommended levels of *vitamin C*

all children were falling short of the recommended levels of *vitamin D*

these nutritional shortfalls tended to be at their worst among children from families on supplementary benefit or Family Income Supplement, the lower income families[5,7]

When it comes to a shortfall in essential nutrients the conclusion is inescapable: children, adolescents and pregnant women living in low-income households have shown generally poor levels of vitamin and mineral intake in survey after survey.

Cheap food = poor health

It may not be surprising that it tends to be lower-income people that are more likely to go short on some essential nutrients. As we have shown, the cheaper sources of calories, such as fast foods, are liable to be short of nutrients.

If the cheap calories are likely to be short on nutrients, and the cheap processed foods are likely to be high in calories, then we would expect people eating low-cost foods to have a greater risk of suffering from the major diet-linked diseases. This appears to be the case. Table 5.4 shows how the main diet-linked diseases are far more common among people on low incomes than they are among people on higher incomes.

But is there any evidence that poor health is related to any particular food being eaten? Can we be certain that fast foods play a significant part in unhealthy diets?

In the two studies which gave the most detail about nutrient shortfalls – the pregnant women in London's East End and the two groups of school children – there is strong evidence that the sorts of food which contributed to their

Table 5.4: **Diet-linked diseases related to social class**

Disease	*most common*	*least common*
Heart and circulatory disease	class V	class I
Tooth disease	class V	class I
Adult cancer	class V	class I
Diseases of digestive system	class V	class I
High infant mortality rate	class V	class I
Low birth-weight	class V	classes I & II

sources: 5.8

poor levels of dietary intake were just the sorts that concern us here – fast foods.

Pregnant women: compared with other mothers, those in the low-income group who were more likely to give birth to low birth-weight babies were found to be eating less fresh vegetables and fish, and instead "relied too heavily on take-away meals".[5/9]

School children: a proportion of the school children studied by the DHSS were eating their mid-day meals at cafes, fish and chip shops and take-away restaurants. The boys in this group showed the lowest average intake of *iron* compared with those eating school meals or home-prepared meals, and had among the lowest intakes of *calcium* and *vitamins A, B1* and *B2*.

The girls who ate in cafes, fish-and-chip shops and take-away restaurants, had the lowest average intakes of *protein, calcium, vitamin A, niacin* and *vitamin D*, and among the lowest levels of *vitamin B2*. In both the boys' and girls' cases, they were getting energy levels not much below others of their age, indicating that they were eating foods with sufficient calories but insufficient essential nutrients; that is, foods with relatively "empty" calories.[5/10]

As the report, *A Survey of the Dietary Intake of British Schoolchildren*, said:

"Older children, especially the girls, who ate out of school at cafes, take-aways and fast-food outlets, etc. had low intakes of many nutrients from these meals, which were not made up by foods consumed at other times of the day. Iron intakes were particularly affected but generally the nutritional quality of the diet consumed by these children was much poorer than those who took school meals, and among the lowest of all groups surveyed." (para. 7.5.2, part)

The chances are high

For many people in the UK the consumption of foods high in fats, especially saturated fats, and the consumption of sugar and salt, is considered to be too high for healthy living. At the same time the consumption of foods providing dietary fibre, such as grains, pulses, fruits and vegetables, is too low.[5/11] We have seen that many fast foods are high in fats, sugar or salt, and low in fibre. Too much of these fast foods may harm your health. Although you probably won't fall ill while holding a fast-food meal in your hands, you could easily increase your chances of an early grave.

If people carry on the eating patterns of the last few decades, the risks of getting a diet-linked disease of one sort or another are relatively high. Few people will escape tooth decay, for example. Over half the population will become medically overweight at some time in their lives. This means a weight which increases the risk of suffering various life-threatening complaints, such as diabetes and high blood pressure.

The chances of suffering various diseases related to diet can be estimated. Table 5.5 shows how, on current health statistics, of every 100 children born today few will escape diet-related illness.

Table 5.5 **Disease expectations for 100 children born today**

(assuming no improvement in our national health statistics)	
52	will become medically overweight by retirement age
29	will be medically overweight by their mid-20s
49	will die of cardiovascular disease
10	of these will die before they reach retirement age
25	will develop diet-related cancers
8	of these will die before retirement age
95	will suffer tooth decay before they reach the age of 15
50	will have lost all their teeth by the time they retire
7	can expect to be clinically malnourished in old age

source 5.12

With all the public awareness of healthy foods and exercise, you may think your chances of being in good health are better than ever before. But this is simply not the case. Heart disease is affecting younger and younger people, and some diet-related cancer figures have also shown significant increases. Two examples are given in Table 5.6.

Table 5.6 **Diet-related disease trends among younger men and women**

(England and Wales, deaths per million people)

	heart disease deaths men aged 35–44	*breast cancer deaths women aged 35–44*
1951	330	216
1961	510	243
1971	660	287
1981	472	267

sources: 5.13

A growing concern

Fast foods are being eaten in greater and greater quantities. Take-away meals alone, excluding the fast foods eaten while sitting in the store, now account for over £1.5 billion in UK sales, totalling hundreds of millions of meals. Although fish-and-chip shops still provide the largest number of take-away meals, the burger bars and fried chicken and pizza restaurants are growing rapidly and together now exceed the sales of the fish-and-chip shops.

Wimpy, the most senior of Britain's fast food chains, has grown to over 430 outlets in a little over 30 years. Kentucky started just over 20 years ago and now has nearly 400 outlets. And McDonald's, which opened its first British store in 1974, now runs nearly 200 outlets and is opening an average of *one new store every 10 days, with plans to continue at this rate for the next 25 years.*

Who is buying all the food they sell? Various surveys have tried to analyse the market for fast food in Britain and have reached broadly similar conclusions. One study[5/14] found

- 36% of students,
- 43% of people aged 15 to 24, and
- 54% of unemployed people

ate fast foods more than twice every week.

Another survey focused on teenagers.[5/15] It found that in the 16 to 18 years age group over 40% said they bought take-away food at least once a week, compared with only 10% of adults in their 40s and 50s. The two largest hamburger chains, Wimpy and McDonald's, were clear favourites with over a quarter of the teenagers saying they would visit one or the other at least once during the week.

So for younger people particularly, fast food appears to

be a significant part of their diet. A recent survey[5/6] of what teenagers actually eat came out with some startling figures:

- 50% of teenagers ate on average more than one hamburger every three days – 150 in a year!
- 95% of teenagers ate on average more than one portion of chips every two days – 200 portions in a year!

And in a separate survey of young adults, it was found that young men aged 15 to 21 in lower income brackets were eating beefburgers as their largest single meat item.[5/17]

A London Food Commission survey of fast food eaters in South London found that nearly a third of fast food eaters said they ate fast food at least once a day. As fast food is obviously becoming a major part of the diet of certain sections of the population it is essential to their health that the ingredients of fast foods are the sort their bodies need. But is it? From what we have seen, the answer is, No!

Teenagers, for example, are still growing. They need nutrient-rich food for healthy growth. Yet by making fast food a key part of their diet they are putting their health at risk.

People on low incomes, particularly, may find fast foods an attractive way of getting a hot meal and eating out. Yet people on low incomes are known to be most at risk of going short of essential nutrients in their general diet. They need to spend what money they have on nutrient-rich food rather than nutrient-poor fast foods.

Later in the book we will show how the big fast food companies are promoting their products directly at young children at home and at school. Young children have an even greater need for high concentrations of minerals and vitamins in their food than older children and adults. If, as the companies hope, the advertising is effective in increasing sales of fast foods to youngsters, then children will increasingly be tempted by foods lower in nutrients than is advisable. Fast foods would become less of an occasional "treat" and more of a way of life.

Ever since the bodies of teenage American soldiers who died in the Korean war were found to be showing the early stages of heart disease, the search has been on for dietary factors which contribute to such early degenerative diseases. Of course you cannot prove conclusively that a burger-and-cola diet will lead directly to these disease symptoms. But you can be pretty sure that such food does not provide all the nutrients needed for an optimum diet and a healthy constitution.

Chapter 6 **We just make it**

We asked over 350 fast food customers in Peckham, London, whether they thought the fast food meal they had just bought was good for them. Only 20% thought that it was. The vast majority did not expect that it would do them any good, even though many were eating such food every day.

Then we asked them *"Would you believe a food company who said the food you had just bought was good for you?"* Only 15% said they would.

Yet in various subtle and not-so-subtle ways the large chains are spending hundreds of thousands of pounds trying to convince us that we should buy their products and that their products will be good for us. They produce glossy literature, they advertise on the TV, they even get into schools. Ironically, it is the customers' own money spent on fast foods which pays for the companies to persuade them to eat even more.

Nutrition leaflets

Fast food companies are well aware of their image as purveyors of "junk" food and much of their advertising budget is spent trying to dispel this image. Health and good living are the favourite themes and one tactic is to mystify us with details of the wonderful vitamins and essential minerals they pack into every item they sell.

McDonald's, Wimpy and Burger King have perhaps gone the furthest in trying to improve the image of fast food by publishing glossy pamphlets extolling the virtues of their menu as a source of valuable nutrients. On the surface, these pamphlets can look very impressive. The company's products appear to contain vast quantities of the nutrients necessary for a balanced diet and a healthy life.

Of course no one denies that foods such as meat, bread, milk and potatoes are a useful part of a balanced diet. But these foods can be diluted in a typical fast food meal, with calories added in the form of extra fat, sugar or refined carbohydrates. The density of the nutrients may be lower, which means consuming more calories to get enough of the other essentials.

Does this mean the companies' pamphlets are lying? No. But they don't present the facts in a way we feel they should be told. They don't show the nutrient density of their food and they make no comparisons with foods which haven't been treated to a fast food catering process. So you can't compare their products with food that hasn't been deep fried or covered in a salty coating or diluted with extra calories during their formulation.

Reading the pamphlets

The following is an example of one company's analysis of a "typical meal combination". The comments and criticisms we make could equally apply to virtually any fast food company's "typical meal".

Large hamburger, large french fries, apple pie, regular Cola

Energy: 1283 calories
Carbohydrate: 152.7 grams
Fat: 64.4 grams
Protein: 32.9 grams
Sodium: 1488mg
Percentage of recommended daily amounts

	Average adult	*Average child 5 to 14 years*
Energy	51%	62%
Protein	53%	65%
Vitamin A	5%	8%
Vitamin C	19%	26%
Vitamin B1	42%	53%
Calcium	44%	34%
Iron	34%	32%

The figures given show how much the product can fulfil the recommended needs of an adult and of a child. The careful reader will see that neither adult nor child is being especially well served. In both cases a greater proportion of daily energy needs (i.e. the calories they need) are being supplied by this meal than are the needs for any of the three vitamins, calcium or iron. The meal gives half the daily calorie needs of an adult and nearly two-thirds the daily calorie needs of a "child aged 5 to 14". Yet the meal does not supply anything like half or two-thirds of vitamin A or vitamin C and doesn't come impressively high in vitamin B1, calcium or iron.

All these nutrients would have to be found in other foods eaten during the day to make up for the low level in this meal. If the eater is not to get seriously overweight then he or she would have to find the nutrients in a form that didn't have another high dose of calories. If you are pregnant, or breastfeeding a child, you may have to eat two or three highly nutritious, low-calorie meals to "balance" a fast food meal.

The second point a careful reader will note is what is *not* included in the table. The meal is short on vitamin B2 (riboflavin), providing less than a fifth of the child's needs.

On the other hand, the fat content is 64.4gm, providing some 45% of the calories, which is well above the 30 to 35% of calories from fat being recommended as an overall maximum for balanced healthy diets by the Department of Health.

Worse still, the meal contains a heavy dose of saturated fat. Some of this may be from the meat, but some will also be coming from the french fries *because the deep frying oil used for french fries is largely made from beef fat*. The Department of Health advises people to eat no more than 10 to 15% of their calories from saturated fat. This meal gives around 20% of calories in the form of saturated fat. The total amount of saturated fat, nearly 28gm, is more than is recommended in any young person's diet *for a whole day* and is virtually all that most adults should consider eating in a day. For anyone to try and balance this meal, no saturated fats should be eaten in any other meal of the day, which is a very difficult task.

The figure for sodium is also high. It is, in fact, equivalent to nearly 4gm of salt *before the eater adds his own*. This is enough for most people's daily needs and approaches the levels recommended by health experts as a daily limit. (Sodium, you may recall, is believed to increase the risk of high blood pressure.)

What emerges is a meal with a high proportion of fat, especially saturated fat, too much salt and a fairly low level of nutrients for the calories provided. The situation stems from simple factors: the fattiness of the burger meat, deep frying in beef fat and the addition of salt in the beef patty, the bun, the sauces and sprinkled onto the fries. So-called "consumer choice" doesn't come into it. These are decisions made by the staff of the largest burger companies. But you wouldn't think there was a nutritional problem by reading their literature.

This example was not chosen in order to isolate one company as the worst offender. It isn't the worst offender by any means. A quick look at the tables in Chapter 4 will show that there are far fattier and far saltier foods. This particular example serves to show the general features of public relations material developed by several of the larger companies. Material such as this can give an encouraging, scientific-looking image to food while ignoring uncomfortable facts that should also be given.

Calculators and complaints

To balance a high-fat, high-calorie fast food meal you would need to find something to eat which has no saturated fat, no salt, high levels of fibre and relatively good levels of vitamins and minerals. To work all that out might need a dietitian's text book, food composition tables and a calculator. The task is beyond the means of most people. Yet the companies contend that fast foods have an important role to play in a balanced diet, a diet which they influence and promote but for which they do not acknowledge their responsibility.

One of the main demands of this book is that the companies should be taking a more responsible attitude to the decisions they make. If you need a balanced diet then you need to have a balanced menu offered when you buy your meal. It is no good having to make up the balance elsewhere, particularly if you don't have a degree in dietetics. What is wanted is to know that what is being offered as a "meal" is nutritionally balanced or can be fairly easily balanced at other meals.

This isn't the first time these issues have been raised. When McDonald's ran a series of advertisements in the United States showing, for example, a bottle of milk, a potato and some fresh minced beef with the slogan "What we are all about", they came under fire from consumer groups and faced legal action in at least three states.

The Washington Post (1/6/87) reported that the Texas State Attorney General had written to the company: "McDonald's food is, as a whole, not nutritious. The intent and result of the current campaign is to deceive consumers into believing the opposite. Fast food customers often choose to go to McDonald's because it is inexpensive and convenient. They should not be fooled into eating there because you have told them it is also nutritious."

The company was told to stop the ads or face a lawsuit. They stopped the ads, but deny any impropriety. According to the newspaper, a McDonald's spokeswoman said: "Our food is of the highest quality, and probably of better consistency than what you could prepare at home".

Catching the children

There is a far more disturbing trend in advertising which the larger fast food companies indulge in: the targeting of their campaigns on young children, often by the use of cartoon or fantasy characters.

So pervasive are these images that one researcher in the USA, looking into children's perceptions of the fast food company characters found that these fantasy figures were more familiar and attractive to children than either their grandfathers, Santa Claus or the local priest!

The reason for attracting children is simple enough. Market surveys have found that children have a lot of influence over where the family eats. Fast food can be a bonus for parents when they are tired and the chance to buy a meal ready-made is welcome. Tired parents, of course, are going to want to avoid the struggle that may be required to persuade their child to go somewhere other than the child's first choice. So they go along with what their child wants. The younger the child, the more difficult it may be to overcome their determination. So it is young children that are the prime target for the companies.

At issue here is not the reasonable need for a parent to get their child fed without a struggle. No parent should feel guilty at the occasional burger or even birthday party outing. What is at issue is the promotion of fast foods as glamorous and desirable products, promoted not just to adults but to the children themselves. Parents can justifiably feel angry rather than guilty: angry because these foods are promoted with no concern for the consequences. No mention is made of the lack of balance or all-round nutrition. As one observer put it, such food is not sold as food in itself but as "an edible part of the entertainment industry".

Unregulated, companies can and will continue to attract children using whatever methods they see fit. In one multinational chain children can "earn" gifts from the company by building up credits for each meal they buy there. Several chains offer benefits to families that bring large numbers to the fast food restaurant, of which the best example is the fast food birthday party. "Free" party gimmicks are provided by the company, and a member of staff keeps the children amused with a well-rehearsed patter.

For parents these parties can be a convenient way of keeping the children happy for an hour or two. For the company it is a reasonable sale of goods and return on the use of the premises and the staff. For the children, it is confirmation of their loyalty to the product's image.

Advertising research shows that customers are prepared to pay 20% more for an advertised product with child appeal even when a less expensive non-advertised product is no different.[6/1]

Of all the fast food chains, McDonald's is the only fast food company in Britain prepared to put the really big advertising budgets behind promotion schemes aimed at young children, spending several millions of pounds on TV commercials and back-up marketing. But the other chains are developing their own forms of "me too" promotions for children.

Kentucky Fried Chicken have been trying out a special menu item: Little Colonel's Meal, presented in its own easy-carry box with cartoon characters and several puzzles. Pizzaland offers Party Time with hats and balloons and for all young customers there are colouring sheets to keep them occupied. The Deep Pan Pizza Company offers special 95p menus for youngsters and gives them a puzzle and colouring sheet, along with a set of crayons. Not to be outdone, Pizza Hut has linked up with Care Bears to produce a special Care Bear Party: for £2.50 each, children get printed invitations, a birthday card, party prizes, a colouring competition, crayons, an organised party game, a Care Bear Birthday Cake and – oh yes – a slice of pizza and a fizzy drink.

Even the quick service restaurants that rely on passing trade, rather than booked parties, are seeing the opportunities a little spending on children can bring. Roadside restaurants like Happy Eater and Little Chef, and motorway service stations such as Granada, are all trying out their own special menus, children's comics, indoor games areas, outdoor playgrounds, and free lollipops to take away after the meal.

An idea launched in the USA, which we might expect to see in Britain soon, is the special Club for children under 10 years old. An identity card is issued to club members, allowing the child a free small cola or other soft drink, provided of course they also buy a main dish.

And as the companies concentrate on the younger eater, we may see mini playgrounds inside fast food outlets. In Manhattan, New York, where floor space is among the most valuable anywhere in the world, McDonald's has sectioned off a play-area in the certain belief that its popularity with children will bring in the customers and amply repay the costs.

Knight in shining armour PR

In the United States, McDonald's has started to extend the image from the realms of TV advertising right into the classrooms of elementary schools. The company developed an "Eating Right, Feeling Fit" campaign with a comic book showing Olympic athlete Mary Lou Retton doing exercises with characters from McDonaldland, plus other materials all bearing the big M company logo. A nutritionist with the Chicago Heart Association commented: "Personally I find it incongruous. McDonald's has incredible chutzpah [cheek]."[6/2]

Pizza Hut has followed a similar theme, focusing on the sporting images and good-worthiness of Sports Aid. Handing over a cheque for £27,000, Pizza Hut launched their National Good Sports Campaign linked in with Sports Aid, involving a series of sponsored events in schools and youth organisations throughout the UK.[6/3]

At a less spectacular level comes a link between Dr Barnardo's Homes for orphans and The Deep Pan Pizza Company. The company organised 21 Christmas parties for Dr Barnardo's children during December 1987 at a cost of several thousand pounds.[6/4]

A different approach taken by McDonald's recently is a new charitable organisation launched under the name Ronald McDonald House Charity. The house in question is to be built near Guy's Hospital, London "to provide parents with a place to stay while their children are undergoing treatment". Launched with a "Buy a Big Mac and support the Charity" day, it is intended that this will be the first of several such "houses" to be built in Britain. Similar schemes have already started in the US, Canada, Australia and Holland.[6/5]

There is, of course, nothing wrong with companies wanting to be seen publicly as caring about children or the environment, or whatever. But their ultimate purpose must be to make people, including children, eat at their restaurants. And, as we have shown, fast foods are not necessarily nutritious and certainly should not be the major part of any growing child's diet.

Designing the product

Far more thought and care goes into designing the food being offered than one might believe. The colouring quality of the fish batter. The shape of the fries packet. The adhesion of the finger-licking coating. All these are the subject of detailed research and careful market testing.

And there's a lot in a name. A "full quarter-pounder" is supposed to sound like a lot more than a 4oz hamburger,

Perhaps conscious of their image as litter-creators, McDonald's recently upstaged their critics by sponsoring the Civic Trust Awards, an annual award designed "to stimulate interest in the appearance of British cities, towns, villages and the countryside" with the award made to the projects which best "improve the surroundings in which we all work, shop, eat and take our leisure".

In a similar vein, Kentucky Fried Chicken has been the sponsor, for some 10 years, of the Keep Britain Tidy Awards.

and perhaps a great deal more than a "110gm burger in a 50gm white flour roll". Then the names are hyped up with tags such as "US-style, Texas-burger, pure 100% beef, in a toasted bun with tasty sesame seed topping".

Cod in batter becomes "Sea-fresh Crispy Cod Bites", pork belly becomes "King Rib Chinese-style". "Barbequed" means coated in a coloured, flavoured sauce which might remind the eater of camp-fires. A "Lincolnshire" sausage may simply mean more sage flavouring, and more fat. A "Crofters" pie never saw the likes of a crofter's kitchen, unless crofters regularly cook with modified starch, textured vegetable protein and use added mono- and di-glycerides of fatty acids. Similarly, there must be very few Cornish kitchens that use monosodium glutamate and tartrazine colouring in their "Original Cornish Pasties"; and the word "traditional" now includes such ingredients as the cotton-industry by-product sodium carboxymethyl cellulose.

A fancy name may be an ad-man's come-on, but the weird and wonderful ingredients are usually there for a purpose. What the industry calls "mouth feel" is the next stage in designing consumer acceptability after the product has been seen and bought. Mouth feel means, of course, what the food feels like in the mouth. This can be influenced by the texture of the product, the temperature it is served at, the flavour, the "bite resistance", the sweetness and saltiness, gummy-ness, stringy-ness, wetness and dryness, and many other -nesses besides.

This is a bonanza for the chemical industry who supply food producers. They supply not just the marvellous additives that make a product look fresh and appetising, but the invisible technical fixes which turn a poor product into an acceptable one. There are dozens of chemicals which can create the required "mouth feel". Not enough moisture? Add an emulsifier to hold in more fat and water, or a phosphate salt to soak up yet more water, or both. Poor flavour? Add some synthetic flavourings, a flavour enhancer, or both.

Dry it out. Soften it up. Make it bend. Make it crumble. Make it melt. Make it sweet. Make it acid. Make it mix properly during production. Make it bake quickly. Make it easy to tip out, to pack, to store, to heat. Out goes Italian cheese and in comes freezable mozzarella substitute, with its hydrogenated oils, emulsifiers, preservatives and anti-caking agents. Out goes fruit and in comes an all-natural soft serve frozen fruit whip with attendant stabilisers, thickeners, flavourings and colourings. After all, say the companies, this is what the customer wants, isn't it? "We only sell the stuff."

Designing the experience

It will soon be commonplace to buy your burgers, hot and ready to eat, in a newsagents shop.[6/6] Or a filling station forecourt. Or late-night grocery. Thanks to microwaves and an enterprising meat industry creating burgers which can be microwaved direct from the deep-freeze, you can soon have burgers wherever you please. But something might be missing.

People don't just go to a fast food restaurant to eat the fast food. They also go because of the atmosphere. The bright gloss and bustle. The warmth, the light, the noise and the action all help a customer to escape from a grey afternoon or a closing pub.

The modern fast food atmosphere is not there by chance and it is not simply created by the customers. When you buy fast foods from a multinational company, the nature of

Selling burgers is the same the world over: the trick is to make people want them by selling them something else, like fun, excitement or sex. Promoting their Double Cheeseburger in Hong Kong, McDonald's commissioned a commercial titled *Two's Company* showing two young boys meeting their girlfriends at a McDonald's outlet. "It's the heart-sell that makes people like McDonald's for its food, folks and fun" claimed the ad company's Creative Director, Hans Ebert. "We not only sell the food but the intangible attributes that make McDonald's more than a fast service restaurant."[6/7] the experience has been carefully and consciously designed. From the colour scheme and the company logo, to the furniture and the spaces between the seats; from the boxes and cups and straws, to the colour of the lighting, its brightness and the contrast with the menu displays. As with any business that wants you to buy their products, all these factors are researched, designed and tested with a specific set of criteria in mind.

The designed experience is intended to be attractive and stimulating. But it shouldn't be so wonderful that customers hang around after they have spent their money. The design has to be pleasant and comfortable but should allow efficient use of production space, customer queuing space, with effective standing to seating ratios, while taking into account cleaning and foot-tripping problems. The wall displays have to tell you the essential bits of information you need before purchasing, but not to encourage you to take too long to make up your mind.

The size of the counter, the number of tills, the space between each one, the standing room around the tills, the distances from tills to tables, the size of tables, the number of chairs and their positions - every item has been scrutinised by trained professionals to ensure no loss of efficiency. The surfaces of the tables, the surfaces of the floors and walls, the arrangement of plants and the ashtrays (and how often they need to be replaced), the average customer's seating need, and the range around the average so that a large adult and a small child can all use the same design of seat: a large company can overlook none of these details if it is to survive the competition.

Burger King in the USA has been trying out a new style for a new customer, redecorating at great cost over 30% of its outlets in an attempt to appeal to the more sophisticated. "We're trying to get all that plastic out. We're adding on greenhouses with real plants. We're using brass railing to queue the customers. Etched glass separates dining areas. Even the trash receptacles are surrounded with oak."[6/8] The aim is to develop a range of identities to suit different markets. People who dislike noise and plastic, and wouldn't think of going to "those type of places" might yet be lured into a brass and oak greenhouse. People with children go to restaurants that can handle and even welcome the younger customer, but there won't be so many plants and mirrors within arm's reach and the tables will be wipe-clean washable.

One McDonald's outlet in America spent $650,000 on an image face-lift, with marble and granite, mirrors and brass. "It's what the public wants" the manager told the

Wall Street Journal.[6/9] "Even when they go for french fries they want it to be an event."

Yet the McDonald's founder, Ray Kroc, insisted that the place was not for loitering in, and banned from all his outlets any pay-phones and any cigarette machines. Hard seats were also the order of the day. For the first few minutes the customer feels relief at just sitting down and concentrates on getting food in the mouth. After a short while, though, the hard plastic and the immovable, screwed down chair begins to have its effect. The average customer gets restless and is off out again. Fast food for the customers. And fast customers for the fast food companies.

Chapter 7 **Big fryers and the small fry**

The fast food phenomenon has arrived and is having a massive effect on our diets, our pockets and our social life. Never before have so many of us eaten so much food so quickly.

Is this all good news for customers? Do we now have greater variety and choice than ever before? Or are we finding that the sheer size of the multinational companies means that we cannot hope to influence their products, and that we have no effective "consumer voice" with which to speak against their activities?

As companies get larger their decisions become more remote from their day-to-day customers. Executives in the United States are deciding the diets of children in Peckham, London. As the companies get more profitable they are able to expand more rapidly. High street sites are converted from local ownership into multinational ownership. As their sales of food increase the large companies' purchasing power can affect the local and the global economy. Whether it is cattle ranching or the ozone layer, the "hamburgerisation" of the diet is having repercussions in each of our lives, from Chicago to Peckham and from Costa Rica to Bangkok.

The largest fast food company in the world, McDonald's, gets 13,000 customers *every minute of the day* on average in its

Table 7.1 **The market for take-away food in Britain**

	sales	*meals*
Fish and chips	£690m	450m
Hamburgers	£410m	380m
Fried chicken	£200m	140m
Pizza	£150m	80m
Others	£350m	200m

sources: LFC and trade estimates. 1987 (ref 7.2)

McDonald's has shown the way for the fast food chains. Arriving in Britain in 1974, they were employing 60 people that year, and their first day's takings at their first outlet in Woolwich brought them less than £40. Being a large company, they could absorb their losses for a long period. By 1984 their workforce had passed the 10,000 mark, and by 1988 it was due to pass 20,000. With even the smaller high street McDonald's expecting over 1000 customers each day, and each customer expected to spend around £1.50, it is not surprising that McDonald's sales in Britain exceed £150m.

were to line up the number of burgers McDonald's alone has sold they would circle the earth *100 times*.[7/1]

In Britain, the story has until recently been less one of hamburgers and more one of fish – the trusty fish and chips which for more than a century have provided take-away meals across the country. Now burgers and fried chicken, pizzas and kebabs, Indian and Chinese cuisines, are starting to replace our traditional eating habits. Although more fish and chips are sold than anything else – we spend about £700m a year eating them – other fast foods are catching up (Table 7.1).

Nearly three out of every five people in Britain are now reported to have a Wimpy outlet near enough for them to visit, and a similar number are now reported to have a McDonald's or a Kentucky Fried Chicken within reasonable reach.[7/3]

Over the last few years the larger food companies, including both catering companies and brewing companies, have been picking off the more successful fast food ideas developed by the smaller organisations and individuals prepared to take the risks. The pattern of ownership is becoming increasingly concentrated, with the larger companies owning more stores, and a greater proportion of the stores, than ever before.

Table 7.2 **McDonald's UK staff levels**

Year	*staff*
1974	60
1975	400
1976	750
1977	1,200
1978	2,500
1979	4,000
1980	4,300
1981	4,800
1982	5,800
1983	9,300
1984	12,000
1985	15,000
1986	18,000
1987	20,000

sources: 7.4

Who owns what on the street

Table 7.3 shows some of the familiar high street fast food names and the big companies that own them.

Some of the world's largest multinational companies have moved into fast food. PepsiCo, the soft drinks giant with a £5bn turnover (1984), bought Kentucky Fried Chicken from R J Reynolds/Nabisco and added it to its Pizza Hut and Taco Bell acquisitions, giving the multi-

Table 7.3 **Ownership of the fast food chains (1987/88)**

Fast food store	*Owned by*
Wimpy Pizzaland Perfect Pizza Crawfords Sayers (plus food products, KP snacks etc)	**United Biscuits**
McDonald's	**McDonald's Corporation**
Aberdeen Steak House Angus Steak Houses American Hamburgers Maxine's Texas Pancake Houses	**Aberdeen Steak Houses Group**
Seafarer Ramsdens Mother Hubbards	**Associated Fisheries**
Baskin Robbins J Lyons Lyons Maid Bertorelli Tonibell Mr Softee	**Allied-Lyons**
Berni Inns Barnaby's (plus foods, hotels, brewing etc)	**Grand Metropolitan plc**
Beefeater Steak Houses Wendy's (UK) TGI Friday	**Whitbread**
Quick Hamburgers	**Whitbread/GB Inno**
Pizza Hut	**Whitbread/PepsiCo**
Taco Bell	**PepsiCo**
Burger King	**Pillsbury**
Casey Jones Travellers Fare	**British Rail***
Le Croissant Pizza Now Cookie Cuisine Gourmet Bakery	**Chestermark**
Crispins Sarah's Manor Catering Chi Chi's Three Cooks British Bakeries (plus various baking, grocery and cereal products, etc.)	**Ranks Hovis McDougall**

Deep Pan Pizza Company Garfunkels Guggenheim's Casa Pasta Big 'Uns Black Angus Steak Houses	**Garfunkels**
Little Chef Happy Eater Julie's Pantry Welcome Break Motorchef (plus hotels, food courts, etc.)	**Trust House Forte**
Kentucky Fried Chicken	**Trust House Forte/ PepsiCo**
Spud-U-Like	**British School of Motoring**
7-Eleven	**Guinness**

* Currently being prepared for privatisation
Sources: 7.5

national company some 18,000 outlets world-wide. They turned to Trust House Forte, itself showing over £1bn annual turnover, to manage their British KFC outlets on a 50–50 basis. Colonel Sanders had incorporated Kentucky Fried Chicken in 1955 and sold it nine years later for some $2m. It was later bought by Hueblin Inc who in turn were bought by R J Reynolds.

Bejam once had five burger outlets that were not making much money. The outlets were sold to Grand Metropolitan (which shows some £4bn annual turnover) and were merged into their chain of Huckleberry's, another burger chain which Grand Met held on franchise from Burger King. But their Huckleberry's outlets were not much helped by the new acquisition, and some three years later Grand Met sold off the lot to United Biscuits (turnover £1.5bn), who have merged them into their Wimpy chain of some 600 outlets world-wide.

Pizzaland was started up in 1973. In 1979 United Biscuits bought the company. United Biscuits then bought up Garner's Steak Houses in 1985 for £7.25m, and turned the acquired premises into Pizzaland outlets. Pizzaland then contributed over £1m to the company's half-yearly profits (July 1986).

Table 7.4 shows some examples of the sizes of the large companies with major fast-food interests:

Table 7.4 **Company sizes**

Company	*Turnover*
McDonald's*	$12,432m (1986)
Pillsbury	$2760m (1987)
PepsiCo (Foods Div.)*	$3118m (1986)
Allied Lyons	£3614m (1987)
Grand Met	£5705m (1987)
United Biscuits	£1954m (1987)
Whitbread	£817m (1987)
Ranks Hovis McDougall	£1544m (1987)
Trust House Forte	£1778m (1987)

* includes franchised sales
sources: 7.6

Franchising

The figures for the companies' own operations may not include the large number of franchised stores that a company may be leasing out. McDonald's, for instance, leases some three-quarters of its 9410 restaurants worldwide to franchisees who pay McDonald's about 11% of their sales in rents and for other head-office services. Adding total sales from the franchised McDonald's to the company-owned McDonald's increases the 1986 sales figures from $4bn to over $12bn. For the company, selling hamburgers is not their only occupation. They are the owners of over $4.8bn worth of property (at their own estimation) while raising over $1bn annually in rent from franchisees. As one observer put it: "McDonald's is a property company which sells hamburgers."[7/7]

Like McDonald's, Wimpy relies heavily on franchise arrangements for its UK base. There are nearly 400 franchised Wimpy restaurants in Britain and only some 33 company-owned restaurants. Even these are seen by the company as part of their franchise operations in the sense that they are used to evaluate design ideas, equipment and management techniques. The company is Britain's largest fast food franchising company with over 300 franchisees ranging from single individuals to large companies.

In most franchising deals, the franchisee enters into an agreement with the parent company to put up a certain amount of capital as a start-up fee and then pays the company an annual fee based on a proportion of the franchisee's turnover or profits. The company gets a highly motivated manager, a lump sum of capital and a return every year whether or not the place makes a profit. The company requires the franchisee to sign a contract to run the franchise for a period of five or, more usually, 10 years, and the franchisee may have to provide a substantial proportion of the start-up fee in cash.

A typical deal with Wimpy's would expect the aspiring millionaire to find some £450,000 to £500,000 as a start-up fee, of which 40% at least must be in cash. They can help arrange a loan with Barclays Bank to cover some of the fee, whereby the franchisee pays off the loan over seven years, at an interest rate 3 to 4% above current base rate. Wimpy like to keep the property in their own names. They help find the premises, take the head lease and then sub-let to the franchisee. Wimpy would provide marketing and operational services and the franchisee must buy all their food products from Wimpy (a practice not permitted in the USA).[7/8]

Kentucky Fried Chicken, until its recent arrangement between PepsiCo and Trust House Forte, was believed to expect some £100,000 start-up fee, plus 4% of monthly sales handed over as royalty fee, plus a further 1.5% of sales as a contribution to advertising costs, plus an obligation to put a further 3% of sales into local promotion and advertising.[7/9]

Pizza Express is another franchising chain. They like franchisees to put up some £110,000 or more to start with. A typical outlet might turn over £250,000, grossing about £40,000 profit if things go as planned. Then the head company takes its cut of this profit at a figure estimated at some £12,000.[7/10]

Success is not guaranteed in the fast food business. Franchisees may be full of good ideas and hard work, but if someone didn't do their market homework, or the "pavement count" (numbers of pedestrians passing over a given time) was too low, the enterprise fails. It is taken in the fast food industry as a rule of success that a customer must be served within three minutes, and no hamburger should sit around waiting for a customer for more than 10 minutes.[7/11]

Despite these problems, and the attendant risks of failure, franchising is likely to remain a popular form of fast food retailing. Smaller companies with bright ideas find it an essential means of rapidly expanding their network without having to find their own massive injections of capital. Essentially they sell the *idea* and put their effort into marketing it nation-wide. They leave to local franchisees the business of managing restaurants that sell the food behind the idea.

For big companies the benefits may be less direct, and indeed Kentucky Fried Chicken has gone the other way, buying up their UK franchised outlets and concentrating them in just one company (Trust House Forte have the franchise for all Kentucky's in the UK). McDonald's has been cautious, initially keeping control of all outlets in Britain, but more recently has considered permitting franchisees to open up in selected sites. Outside the UK McDonald's has emphasised and encouraged franchising and joint venturing in countries as diverse as Japan and Yugoslavia, France and Singapore, Turkey and Argentina; some 45 countries in all.[7/12]

Global Burgers Inc

The success of Coca Cola's expansion from its United States base into a world-wide multinational is largely attributed to the contract it won with the US Forces during the Second World War. Agreeing to supply the all-American military conscripts wherever they were to be posted proved to be a heaven-sent opportunity to open up markets for the drink across the globe.

The lesson was not lost on the burger chains and Burger King managed to get the contract to open up fast food restaurants in US Army and Air Force bases world-wide. Not to be beaten easily, McDonald's then managed to get the lucrative US Navy contract, giving it 300 Navy and three Marine bases at home and abroad and on the ships themselves. By 1986 they had opened 44 hamburger bars for US forces around the world.[7/13]

But for McDonald's the military connection is not a means to conquer the fast food world. If anything it is the least of their global concerns. They have already expanded across the world at an unprecedented rate that has seen average sales increasing 16% annually for five years. They now control nearly 10,000 restaurants world-wide with two-thirds of these under franchise agreement. A quarter of these restaurants are outside the USA and the proportion is growing. Non-USA sales of McDonald's products grew an all-time record of 35% in 1986.[7/14]

Nor is McDonald's alone. Kentucky Fried Chicken claims nearly 6000 outlets across the world and won an important public relations coup in 1987 by opening the first overseas fast food restaurant in China. Its sister organisation, Pizza Hut, has over 5000 units while the third PepsiCo chain, Taco Bell, has a further 2400.[7/15]

Wimpy has turned to the international market relatively recently. They now claim some 140 stores in 21 countries, including a breakthrough in India. For most Indians, the idea of eating a hamburger made of beef is taboo. Wimpy's breakthrough in New Delhi has come with the development of two products: the lamburger for those that eat meat but not beef, and a vegetable burger for the large numbers who eat no meat at all.

This may be good news for the companies, and it may even bring a moment of joy to the new fast food eater, but is it really operating in the interests of consumers across the world? As the Philippine research institute IBON commented:

"*... whether pizzas and hamburgers are here to replace* puto *and* kutsinta *may sound to be a non-issue amid these critical times when people can hardly afford even basic necessities. Nonetheless, considering that the Philippines' fast food business, which generated P$2bn in 1982 is led by big American food chains, a legitimate issue regarding foreign food chains arises: what is their impact on our economy and culture? And some corollary issues: is donut- or hamburger-making a strategic technology that must be learnt by Filipinos? Don't these food chains' imported posters and paper bags drain our precious dollars? As with most foreign enterprises, these foreign food chains' schemes are best understood in the light of their global operations.*"[7/16]

The impact on the world's eating habits of fast food operations and the effects of this on the world's food supplies is significant and increasing. The *Malay Mail* asked whether people "long used to satay, koay, teow and thosai, have begun to also go for hamburgers, fish and chips, fried chicken and pizzas?" They reported the rapid rise of fast foods in Malaysia during the early 1980s, growing at an estimated 20 to 30% each year. The trouble, they report, is that "unlike indigenous industries, these chains import most of their raw materials, and therefore contribute less to the economy..." The effects on the nation's health were also called into question: "... the high amount of fats in fast foods can raise cholesterol levels and contribute to a greater incidence of heart disease."[7/17]

A similar pattern of growth is shown in other countries in Asia. Hong Kong statistics show that by 1985 burgers and pizzas had outgrown fried rice in sales figures. While Chinese restaurants were recording falling sales, fast food chains were showing increases averaging some 32% annually.[7/18]

Taiwan, too, has seen a rush of multinational fast food chains into its high streets. McDonald's opened its first outlet there in 1984 and had 12 open by the end of 1986. US chain Wendy's started in 1985 with plans for 25 outlets in just two years. Kentucky Fried Chicken is aiming for 50 stores inside 10 years.

Other countries have seen a similar invasion of burger giants and deep fried chickens. McDonald's alone started

Are we all living in McDonaldland?

Visiting Thailand prior to its first McDonald's store opening, the company's vice president, Thomas A Gruber, addressed a packed press conference. "We are confident Thailand will be a good place to conduct business" he said. "We are proud to be here – soon to be the 32nd McDonaldland country."[7/19]

business in 10 new countries in 1984–86 and added over 1100 new stores during that time. Thailand, Turkey, Mexico and Venezuela all saw McDonald's arrive and prosper.

But it must be Japan that takes the Mac-award: with an estimated 43,000 staff working in nearly 600 McDonald's stores, Japan has almost as many McDonald's outlets as the whole of Western Europe. In a little over 15 years the Japanese franchisee (working a 50–50 deal with the parent company) has built up an annual turnover exceeding $600m.[7/20]

In a fascinating insight to the psychology of consumers, franchise director Den Fujita comments:

"Japanese always have a dual attitude to things foreign. On the one hand they have an inferiority complex about foreign ways, on the other they feel themselves superior. That is one reason why our McDonald's staff are encouraged to speak a few words of English to each other for the benefit of mostly uncomprehending customers. But display of the US flag on the premises is at all times barred. One Japanese youngster travelling abroad saw a McDonald's in Chicago and exclaimed 'Do they have them here, too?'

"The non-MacDonald's generation is on its way to the cemetery, and will be replaced by a new breed of elders who have eaten burgers from their youth."[7/21]

The image of the cemetery may be more apposite than Fujita realises. According to the director of the Framingham, Massachusetts Heart Study, Dr William Castelli, the traditional Japanese diets were far healthier than their newly acquired "fast food" diets imported from the USA. "The Japanese traditionally had a very low fat diet, consuming only about 30gm a day. Now that we're sending the Japanese our beef in return for cars, urban Japanese are now eating about 60gm of fat a day and the heart disease rate for city-dwelling Japanese is about four times higher than it was 35 years ago."[7/22]

Hamburgers should not be isolated as the sole target for dietary criticism. Despite the reputation of chicken as a low fat meat, a typical serving of fried chicken can be 24% fat, with the fat contributing 60% of the calories in the meal. Japan has taken to fried chicken in a big way: Kentucky chickens annually.[7/23] Far from turning into a new breed of fast food-eating elders, Japanese youngsters are more likely to turn into Japanese cardiac cases.
likely to turn into Japanese cardiac cases.

As Annalies Allain, of the International Organisation of Consumer Unions has written:.

"Where purchasing power is low, it is all the more important to protect healthy eating habits. Asian street foods still provide many dishes that are liked and give a good nutrient value for money... For low-income consumers, food represents the single largest budget item. As much as 80% of the family income may be sent on food...

"When asked for a single piece of advice for future Asia, Mahatma Gandhi said: 'Reduce your wants and supply your needs! Our needs make us vulnerable enough, why increase our vulnerability?'"[7/24]

Re-shaping the world's diet

The opening of a McDonald's in Thailand was perhaps little different to the opening of a McDonald's anywhere else in the world. But the franchisee did admit that there were significant supply problems as he couldn't get all he needed from local sources. Dej Bulsuk, managing director of McThai Co Ltd, said that for at least six months McDonald's would be importing beef from Australia until a local supplier could take over. They were also starting up experiments in the north of the country to produce the right potatoes.[7/25]

Underlying these admissions is the "hamburgerisation" of food supplies, of which Thailand is only a small example. Potatoes are not a native Thai vegetable but have been introduced and, in this case, the production is closely geared to McDonald's needs. Nor is Thailand's traditional beef supply of the right quantity and quality for the burger's specifications. So Thailand's food supplies must change. Ironically, three days after the newspaper report of the McThai opening, McDonald's sold its world-wide 50 billionth hamburger. Two years later, in November 1986, the 60 billionth McDonald's hamburger was sold.

Even in Britain the potato growers are coming under pressure to increase their production of just one particular variety that suits fast food processing, the Californian Russett Burbank, with over 4000 acres being newly planted with this variety in 1986 alone.[7/26]

These burgers need meat and wheat and the fries need potatoes. Meat above all else needs land devoted to cattle grazing or production of grains for animal feed. According to one estimate, it takes 15 to 20 kilograms of grain to produce one kilogram of beef.[7/27]

Otherwise, beef production requires extensive ranching land. Costa Rica alone exports 42 million kilograms of beef annually to the USA in order to support the growing sales of burgers and other beef products. To provide this amount of beef, Costa Rican landowners have been burning thousands of square miles of natural tropical forests at a rate estimated at 50,000 to 70,000 hectares each year with devastating effects:

"The removal of the forest cover leads to soil erosion and much of the new pasture turns to scrub within a few years. As a result, one third of the country is now covered with pasture or infertile scrub. Small farmers are squeezed out as large ranches expand, but very few jobs are created on beef ranches because it takes only one person to look after a thousand cattle. This has perilous consequences for the local economy."

"Although fast food chains won't own up to using beef from Central and South America (aware that this is very unpopular with the US ranching and feedlot interests), there is no doubt that this 'hamburger connection' is a reality. Costa Rican ranchers have readily confirmed it."[7/28]

One problem is that, once imported into the USA, foreign-produced and domestically-produced beef are not distinguishable. Even if strenuous attempts are made to ensure that only domestic beef is used for US hamburgers, beef exported from the US to other countries may include such Central American beef. Furthermore, even if only US-produced beef is used, that too may well have been fed on imported grain, which itself came from de-forested and peasant-evicted areas of Latin America.

American campaigners have turned their attention on the number two burger company, Burger King. Pointing out that cattle ranching in Central America would be difficult without the support of US banks and finance houses, the organisation *Earth First!* claimed that Burger King imported rainforest beef. In 1987 Burger King's US consumer Relations Supervisor wrote in reply to a consumer's query that "Burger King does not specify the location of beef sources." The spokesperson added, "Costa Rica has been rigidly enforcing an internal land use policy and it is our understanding that there has been no widespread destruction of rain forests."[7/31]

British McDonald's are reported to use only EEC-produced beef for their hamburgers.[7/29] But EEC beef is grown on cattle-feed which is itself imported from countries such as Brazil and, according to Compassion in World Farming, drought-ridden Ethiopia.[7/30]

Ozone

A great deal of design went into the creation of the heat-retaining polystyrene containers which the burger chains usually favour. According to Friends of the Earth, the foam-constructed containers contain chlorofluorocarbons which damage the protective ozone layer which encircles the earth.

With some 4 million hamburgers eaten each week in Britain[7/32] plus many other fast foods served in similar polystyrene containers, ozone damage is potentially quite serious. World-wide the figures are certainly very serious. McDonald's alone sells in the region of 12,000 hamburgers every minute,[7/33] which is a lot of polystyrene in a year. The containers weigh about 7gm, making some 84 kilograms of polystyrene every minute - over 44 million kilograms in a year from just one company's products.

McDonald's won't say if their containers are made with chlorofluorocarbons. But the company's London spokesperson initially said that because it was "not firmly established" that the chemicals were causing these atmospheric problems there was no need to consider not using them.[7/34] Discoveries during 1987 that there is a gap in the ozone layer above Antarctica fuelled the environmental campaigns against chlorofluorocarbons and increased consumer pressure. Within a few months McDonald's changed their position. "We decided," announced McDonald's, "to change sooner rather than later." Wimpy also started to negotiate re-formulation with their suppliers. "We don't want to be left behind," a spokeswoman for the company said.[7/35]

No company wants to be left behind a market trend, of course. But for every company the key marketing question has to be: *Which way is the trend going?* We shall take a few risks by predicting some forthcoming fast food trends in the next chapter.

Chapter 8 **Fast food futures**

Are Mexican chillies the next hot fashion? Or is it to be home-delivered pizzas? Will sandwiches and salads ever see the light of day?

There are two ways of predicting the longer-term trends in fast foods in Britain. One is to look at what is happening in other countries, especially in the USA where fast foods hold an even bigger chunk of food sales than they do here, and where some of the largest fast food companies are based.

The second is to look at the new forms of technology that the food industry is developing and ask whether they may have an influence on what we will be offered as tomorrow's taste sensation.

Back in the USA

American research suggests a trend among consumers to want to know what they are eating, with definite turn-offs like "bleached", "emulsified", "irradiated", "processed" and "preserved".

"Consumer research reveals that to the consumer, additives equal chemicals equal cancer," says one US commentator. "It leads to an insistence on good quality, especially from younger age groups. Wendy, one of the most successful fast food chains, now proclaims the availability of light, low calorie, food, and salad bars are springing up everywhere."[8/2]

Salad bars are not a new idea. They have been tried in fast food restaurants across the United States and Europe. McDonald's boasts an extensive range of salads available to customers, *but not in Britain.*

The health trend has yet to penetrate to the senior levels of these big companies' British management. You can buy fast food salads in the burger bars of Strasbourg and Saskatchewan, but not in Salford or Southwark. Not in the hamburger stores, or the chip shops, that is. But the pizza chains are developing salad bars as an attractive sideline, so there is no excuse for the others not to try. The trouble is,

One development in the USA is a "piggy-backing" of two fast food companies in one outlet: Mexican chain Taco John's, for example, has linked in with Bresler's 33 Flavor ice cream chain to sell both products on the same site. Similarly Tastee-Freez ice cream has joined with Mister Donut to sell both products to the same customer at the same time. Where the products do not compete it clearly makes sense to the companies involved. In Britain, however, a different version of multiple sales under one roof has developed in the form of the *food court*.

Food courts give a customer the appearance of offering a variety of foods which can be selected from the various different restaurants around the court and a choice of attractive seating areas shared by all customers. I select a burger, you have a pizza, and we'll follow it with a gateau and coffee. We get our food from different "stores" around the court and sit together where we like.

But while we may think we are choosing from a variety of different outlets, in reality some of the courts are actually owned and run by just one company. There are eight fast food "eating experiences" around the seats at the Victoria Station Food Courtyard and all eight outlets are owned by Trust House Forte.[8/1]

At first there may seem to be little wrong with such a conglomerate cafe. But if the prices start to rise (and they aren't exactly rock bottom anyway) or the quality of the food deteriorates, then where is the competitor who can set up a cheaper outlet in among these courts? What effect will they have on nearby, single restaurants, except to drive them out of business? The impression that they may give, of offering a real choice of competing products, can be misleading and may not be in the customers' best interests.

even the salads may be doused in sugary, salty, fatty sauces loaded with benzoates and sulphites so they stay fresh-looking. If you fancy fresh raw veg, then you have to make it clear: "Give us salads and no messing!"

One report suggests that the recent US consumer interest in eating healthily is spawning a new demand for sea-food products. Haddock and cod lead the list of favourites, but other fish and shell-fish are coming in fast. As George Torggler, shell-fish distributor for American Original Foods, is reported as saying: "Today, in America, if you want to stay healthy, it's clams or bananas."[8/3]

In the meantime, the low-calorie drinks have come in big in the States. Diet Coke, launched in 1982, has taken the number one place in low-calorie drinks, and the number three place in all soft drinks sold in the USA.[8/4] Its low-calorie status makes it appealing to weight-conscious eaters, though its lack of nutrients and list of other chemicals makes some health-conscious drinkers hesitate. Aware of this, Coca Cola are reported to be considering mass-marketing various alternatives: the White Cola, a colouring-free version, is one idea, while a special hypotonic drink for athletes is another.[8/5] Another possible front-runner is an added-vitamin cola aimed at pleasing parents.

Health technology

A "healthy" burger has already become a feature of UK giant, Wimpy, in the form of their Beanburger. Other attempts to imitate meat have been tried by various companies: one burger sold to help dieters is reported to be a low-calorie, vegetarian soyaburger, reviewed quite unfairly by one journalist as:

"Free from meat, colouring, preservatives and artificial flavouring it looks like a burger, cooks like a burger and tastes like a beermat."[8/6]

How to make it more tasty; that's the question, and plenty of firms have the answer. The companies who make the relishes are out looking for health-oriented customers, with low-calorie mustard, slimmers' mayonnaise and oil-free vinaigrette being hyped up for the diet-conscious. Thanks more to the chemical industry than to any natural product, these concoctions can be made to appear like their more traditional counterparts by careful use of emulsifiers, flavouring agents, artificial sweeteners and the like. But you ain't seen nothing yet!

Still in the laboratory, but under application for a sales licence, comes *sucrose polyester*, or SPE. It is not, despite its name, a sugar. It is a *fat*. But it isn't a fat as far as our stomachs are concerned, because our stomachs cannot digest the stuff, and so it has no calorie value. It is the dieter's dream product – a no-calorie fat!

One company in particular has been pouring money into its laboratories trying to make the perfect SPE product – the detergent and soap giant, Procter and Gamble. It has named its version of SPE *olestra* and in 1987 filed an application with the US Food and Drugs Administration to sell the product as a food to caterers and the general public, suggesting that olestra could take the place of 35%

of the fat in cooking oils and 75% of the fat used in commercial deep fat frying and fried snack foods.[8/7]

But this dream product – fat that looks, feels, tastes and cooks like fat but isn't fattening – has not yet been approved and consumer groups in the United States, notably the Centre for Science in the Public Interest, have raised several concerns about its use.

One apparent benefit of olestra is that it appears to lower the level of cholesterol in the blood. But on the negative side, it also appears to lower the level of fat-soluble vitamins, such as vitamins A, D and E.

According to Procter and Gamble spokesman Donald Tassone, the final product will include added vitamin E in an attempt to replace what olestra removes. "But," he added, "we don't see any need to add A, since most people get more than enough of that vitamin."[8/8]

Unfortunately, for just those people who eat a lot of commercially prepared fatty foods (including many fast food products) the effect of cutting down on vitamin levels could be the difference between getting just enough nutrients and being chronically deficient. We have seen earlier in this book that both vitamins A and D are at low levels in school children who get their mid-day meals from cafes, take-aways and chip shops. The suggestion that 75% of the fat in the products they are eating may be replaced by a sucrose polyester, potentially lowering what little vitamin A and D they are now getting from their food, raises serious questions about whether the product should be permitted.

No-fat, no-sugar, no-starch

Besides the possibility of a no-calorie substitute for fat, there are other developments in food technology. For many years sugar has been replaced by various synthetic sweeteners, but these have not been as successful as the manufacturers would like. In America, labelling laws have led to some public disquiet about them. Saccharin has to be labelled on packets as a potential "hazard to health" in the USA as it has been linked to cancer in laboratory animals. Aspartame has to be labelled in the USA as a hazard for people suffering from the hereditary disease phenylketonuria. UK labelling laws do not require either of these warning statements although the same risks apply in the UK as in the USA.

Now the sugar industry is developing a new substitute which actually uses sugar but changes the structure of the molecule. Sucralose, a re-arranged sugar molecule with added chlorine, is Tate and Lyle's answer to the artificial sweetener companies. The company sees their product as a replacement for aspartame in soft drinks and for sugar in cooked products such as cakes and biscuits. A licence to market sucralose was applied for in early 1987 with the hopes that it would be on sale by the end of the year. But at the time this book went to press approval had not yet been granted.

With the possibility of no-fat fat and no-sugar sugar, there remains still the scourge of the health conscious: refined flour. But in the United States even this bastion of bad calories may be falling. Fluffy cellulose is the name, a product made of the indigestible parts of all plants: cellulose. It has the characteristics of flour but without the calories.

So now for the ultimate doughnut: mix fluffy cellulose with sucrose polyester, add sucralose to sweeten and fry in more sucrose polyester. Sprinkle on some synthetic flavourings and there it is, the zero-calorie food of the decade. Zero nutrients, too. So somewhere we still have to find the nourishment we need to live. Easy. Sprinkle it on! Add some multi-vitamin and mineral compounds with concentrated fibre gel and you have your entire supply of dietary requirements.

No-one can yet say what long term effects on human health these new products might have. To meet our need to cut down the fat in our diet industry has responded not by returning to healthier foods but by adapting the molecules of fat so they can, supposedly, be used more safely. We shall, it seems, be encouraged to eat food from chemical plants rather than farm-grown plants.

Faster food, everywhere

Future fantasies aside, there are some aspects of technology that are having a more immediate impact on eating patterns. One of these is the familiar microwave oven.

It has long been the food producers' dream to be able to get their products into our hands with the products looking their best. With fast food, the method has been to employ a lot of cheap labour in a "factory line" kitchen, churning out the products to a waiting queue of hungry eaters.

But with the developments in food freezing and re-heating technologies, it is becoming possible to put food straight from the deep freeze into the microwave. A minute or two later you have a fresh-looking hot meal. Little labour and capital costs are needed, just a retail deep-freeze and a couple of microwave ovens. All of it is established technology with low power consumption.

So the day is now dawning when you can pop into your

newsagent and walk out with a hot burger or pizza. Or grab a hot meal in a petrol station forecourt, with everything being re-fuelled at one stop.

But if this seems unappealing then consider this: a machine like a coffee dispenser which serves a plate of steaming pasta and sauce. The pasta is cooked and served in 50 seconds, thanks to the development of hollow spaghetti and a pressure cooker to match it.

It can be installed anywhere that has a tap and an electric point. It can sit on a shop counter and if the customer takes the food away to eat elsewhere there is no need to provide seats.

New communications technology also plays a role in speeding up our fast food delivery. The staff at the front of the restaurant tap your order into their mini-transmitter and back in the kitchen the order comes up on the display. By the time you or the waiter have gone to collect it, it is ready.

But with home deliveries of cooked food expanding, the next move may be for smaller street-side hot food carts to get into the lunch-time office delivery market, using portable radio telephones to take the orders.

Undesirable growths

In all the razzmatazz about new products and new technology, there is one area of growth which the catering trade is reluctant to publicise: *food poisoning*. It is the most tangible and immediate aspect of an unhealthy diet which can be linked to a specific product eaten at a specific time.

Overall rates of food poisoning in Britain have been rising since figures were first collected in a systematic way after the last world war. The numbers of cases crept up during the 1950s and 1960s and began to rise alarmingly during the 1970s. Now the trend has continued at unprecedented rates, with some 22,000 outbreaks being reported to the authorities in 1987 and an estimated two million people possibly being affected annually.[8/9]

Fast food outlets have had their share of outbreaks and are often viewed by the public as likely to be harbouring unsavoury microbes. There is little evidence, however, that they are any worse than other types of restaurant. Food poisoning usually stems from a combination of poor stock rotation and stock monitoring, poor hygiene and lack of training on the part of food handlers and the use of infected meats in the preparation of the recipes. This last one is, in a sense, the major hazard, since there would be less risk to consumers if the original food was not infected before it arrived at the restaurant. We need to look to animal rearing practices to see why food poisoning is becoming such a serious issue in the 1980s.

The principal cause of food poisoning is *salmonella*, one of a range of microbes which live in dead meat and breed when they reach the warmth of, first, the kitchen, and then the perfect environment of a human stomach. A survey of frozen chickens in 1979 found nearly 80% to be infected with salmonella and there is no evidence that this rate has substantially dropped since then.

Intensive rearing of animals has become commonplace in Britain. The average size of a herd of pigs is now over 1000 animals and the average flock of chickens numbers an incredible 29,000.[8/10] To prevent the spread of diseases among such large numbers requires the use of drugs, principally antibiotics, in the daily feed. But microbes can quickly adapt and new, resistant strains develop which will survive the onslaught of antibiotics.

Modern farming practices are also likely to expose livestock to salmonella and other food poisoning microbes by recycling animal products back into the animal feed: blood, bone, offal and even manure. (For more details on animal feed, such as the cardboard, bones and chicken excrement fed to cattle in the USA, see Orville Schell's *Modern Meat*.[8/11]) Although this compound feed should be sterilised during manufacture, it may not get sufficiently heated and may also be poorly separated from the unsterilised mixture.

These forms of potential meat infection are only the start of the chain. When the animals come to the slaughter they face an array of machinery designed to make their death and their conversion into butchers' and caterers' carcasses as fast and efficient as possible. What happens, then, if a beast or bird is found to be badly infected when it is slaughtered? In theory the whole production line has to stop, the offending carcass removed and all the equipment which touched it should be cleaned and sterilised. This may or may not be done: official figures do not reveal such good or bad practices. But if the carcass is infected (and salmonella infection is virtually invisible), then it will clearly carry on down the line and the equipment will spread the bacteria on to every piece of meat that follows.

Animals are delivered for slaughter in large numbers. For example, a typical figure for poultry is 10,000 at a time. To do this means running large, industrialised abattoirs with a high throughput. Staff may be paid at piece-rates, earning more for faster work. In 1986 EEC inspectors complained about British abattoirs, saying they were run too fast, staff moved too freely between "clean" and "dirty" areas and that there was a general lack of awareness of basic hygiene, allowing gross contamination of meat during dressing.[8/12]

While the meat remains raw, it may remain infected. But once processed it should, we might expect, be free of infection. Unfortunately, statistics don't bear this out. Processed meat products have been implicated in half of all food poisoning outbreaks during recent years. One problem is that some meat products are bulked out with mechanically recovered meat (MRM), a meaty slurry made by mechanically stripping every minute scrap of meat, cartilage and sinew still clinging to the bones after the main cuts have been removed. MRM is, according to the government Food Standards Committee, a chemically less stable product than carcass meat and "presents a greater microbial risk". As MRM need not be declared on the labels of products as anything other than "meat", we cannot say here which, if any, meat products in the fast food sector include it.

The food industry argues that the recent concern over chemical preservatives, and the "healthy eating" trend towards reducing the chemicals in our food, is part of the cause of food poisoning outbreaks. They hope to persuade us to let them keep adding the preservatives as their means of stopping their poor hygiene practices from affecting us. In fact the incidence of food poisoning outbreaks has been increasing for decades, long before industry responded to consumers' demands for less chemical preservatives in their food. It is the changing nature of food production which has led to the problem and consumers should not be made to feel they must eat preservatives to solve the food industries' problems.

Last in the food chain is the caterer where the food is finally prepared and served to customers. It is estimated that caterers are responsible for one in every four outbreaks of food poisoning. Top of the league come restaurants, including fast food outlets, and buffet receptions, followed by catering in big institutions such as hospitals.

Areas that fast food operators need to keep a watch on are the cooking and warm-holding tasks, to ensure that food is thoroughly cooked and not kept for long periods at room temperature. They should also watch their stores, ensuring that food is kept cold or frozen and that stock is not left over from previous batches. To their credit, many of the larger chains have developed practices which minimise risks and have rules to ensure that old food is destroyed. The rules often require products to be destroyed if they have sat for more than a fixed amount of time after cooking, sometimes as short as 10 minutes. They also forbid staff from removing old food from the premises.

Whether these rules are observed in practice is not documented. The budgets available for environmental health officers' inspection of premises is insufficient for complete coverage of all outlets on a routine basis, so only partial sampling can be done. At least a quarter of take-away restaurants will not be visited from one year to the next even though about one in eight products such as meat pies and sausages are typically found to be contaminated.

A remaining problem is that of ensuring that staff are properly trained in food handling and food hygiene. As fast food operations tend to employ people prepared to accept low pay and erratic hours, and as the majority stay less than a few months in the job, it is highly probable that their training will be minimal. The Institute of Environmental Health Officers is currently urging the Ministry of Agriculture, Fisheries and Food to introduce food hygiene tests among all food handlers.[8/13]

If you have any suspicions about food poisoning then contact your doctors, for your own health, and your local authority Environmental Health Department, for the sake of other people's health.

Food poisoning: what you can do

- Don't hold on to your fast food: eat it straight away. Taking it away, keeping it and then re-heating it is asking for trouble.
- Do not accept food which looks poorly cooked, especially chicken or beef. If the chicken looks too pink ask for another piece to be cooked for you.
- The microbe *bacillus cereus* favours re-heated rice and also populates some salad bars, and there have been cases of *salmonella* poisoning resulting from eating uncooked bean sprouts. Take a good look at your take-aways before you eat them.

Environmental Health Officers and Trading Standards Officers are the responsible enforcers of the food hygiene and food standards laws and can be contacted through your local town hall. These are also the people to contact if you find foreign objects in the food (like the piece of glass found by a woman in a burger in Dublin[8/14]), or if the premises are unhygienic (like the burger bar in Lambeth fined for having dirty equipment[8/15] and the grease-encrusted hot-dog stall in Farnborough[8/16]), or if the food is not quite what it ought to be (like the diet cola made with sugar which another burger outlet sold in Hereford[8/17]).

Chapter 9 **Working the line**

As a fast food customer you may not give a second thought to the person who serves up your order. But if you are to start demanding changes in the nature of the food you are being offered, as this book may encourage you to do, you will find that you are indirectly also making demands on the way that the food is produced.

Production methods which produce foods fast may not be conducive to preparing food which is healthy. If we want changes in the menus we will also have to press for changes in cooking practices, such as less deep-fat frying and more salad preparation. Menus with greater variety on them may require greater staff attention to each customer. Depending on how management respond, this could mean greater pressure on the present staff or it could mean an increase in the number of staff employed.

So when, as consumers, we urge that changes are made to the food we are served, we will be implying that changes should be made to what is in the food, how it is brought to us, how it is prepared and even in what forms and wrappings it is served. This implies changes not only in the restaurant but possibly all the way back to the factories, farms and forests. But it is in the restaurants that we shall be starting our campaign. Changes are often resisted by entrenched interests, on both workforce and management sides. So we need to have a good understanding of what it is like working in fast foods if we are to understand sympathetically why workers might initially show little interest in a call for change.

In this chapter we will take a look at the experiences of fast food workers and the sort of conditions they work in. The London Food Commission was set up on the basis of a joint approach between consumers and food workers, in the belief that with the interest and support of food workers any consumer demands will be more powerful and effective. In turn, it is also important to show that changes do not necessarily imply threats.

Criticising the fast food industry does not necessarily

imply an attack on jobs, but rather a desire to see that what is produced is what is really needed and wanted. If this is the case, then the producers of such food will be in very secure jobs as products which are really needed and wanted will find a ready market. It is our concern to ensure that fast foods are of a sort that provide for these needs, and hence also provide good, secure jobs. This does not always appear to be the case at present.

Have a nice day: the smiles and fries machine

"It's all artificial. Pretending to offer personal service with a smile when in reality no one means it... All they want to do is take the customer's money as soon as possible. That's what it's all designed to achieve."
Sheila, 19, fast-food worker[9/1]

"Everything is controlled. There are 19 different steps in making French fries. They tell you which direction to shake the salt in... You have to hustle and you work as a team. If you go too slowly you let everybody else down."[9/2]

"You should only fry four pieces of fish in the basket; when the manager is not looking you put five, or six or seven. You constantly try and build up stock by cutting corners. Sometimes the managers themselves turn a blind eye, because they know that if you didn't cut corners you couldn't keep up with the customers."[9/3]

Fast food work, especially in the multinational food chains, is supposed to be based on high technology, assembly-line production, making identical products across the country and across the world, with each job broken down into the smallest steps requiring minimal skill. But the reality can be different. As one ex-worker commented: "The professors have got it wrong. The food is produced by sheer old fashioned hard labour. Technology is restricted to the basic food production in the factories that supply the fast food shops and to the mechanisms in the kitchens that control the heat of the grills and frying vats. The rest depends almost entirely upon the efforts of the labour force."[9/4]

The same worker goes on to describe her colleague's endlessly repetitive job:

"It begins when he takes 12 burger patties from the box in the fridge by the side of the grill, banging them on the edge to separate them, then laying them down on the grill, two rows of six. He presses the button which times the cooking stages; when the buzzer goes he sears the patties with the sear tool, wipes the sear tool, presses the button again; when the buzzer goes he turns the patties over with a spatula, wipes the spatula, presses

FFF—H

the button; when the buzzer goes he sprinkles the salt and onion onto each pattie, lifts them off with the spatula and places them on the dressed buns, wipes the spatula, takes the scraper to remove the burnt meat and excess fat off the grill, wipes the scraper, gets more frozen patties from the fridge and taps them on the edge to separate them."[9/5]

Jobs like these need little prior experience or training. As in much of the catering industry, the cheapest end of the labour market can be tapped: young school leavers with no work experience and little ambition. The pay levels are correspondingly low, and well below the current EEC "decency threshold" for a single person's wage of £135.25p per week (1988) which works out at over £3.35p per hour for a 35 to 40 hour week. This is the level considered the lower limit for wage rates for a decent standard of living. Few fast food companies offer anything like that level of pay, with rates of pay between £1.60p and £2.20p per hour being typical of the larger fast food companies in the London area.[9/6] By way of perks, several companies allow staff 30p-worth of food for every hour they work: "One of the best things about working for McDonald's is the food. When you have a break you may have a meal of your choice..."[9/7]

Wages Councils set the minimum wage rates for the catering industry, including fast food workers. They also regulate the overtime rates, the limit to the normal working week (currently 39 hours) and any staff accommodation costs. Other aspects of employment conditions which they used to be responsible for have been removed from them in 1986. Besides these controls, fast food companies must comply with various employment acts, such as the 1950 Shops Act which sets overtime limits, employment during unsocial hours limits, breaks between shifts, lunch breaks, and the maintenance of employment records.

There is little hard information pin-pointing any cases where these rules have been broken by fast food companies. One major attempt to find out what was happening was undertaken by Hounslow Trading Standards Department. They did a lightning raid on 11 different fast food outlets in their locality and found:

- every store infringed the regulations in one way or another
- in five cases the infringements were minor, but in six they were more serious, and included:

  - young women (under 18) made to work after 10 p.m.
  - less than 45 minutes allowed for lunch

- failure to record hours worked or breaks taken

- management confessed to being ignorant of the legislation
- in one case the staff handbook was wrong on lunch break allowances
- written warnings were sent to the six worst offending stores, and re-visits were threatened.

"It's disgusting that local employers are exploiting young people in this way just to maximise their profits," commented Councillor Hunt, Hounslow's Chair of Health and Consumer Protection. He called on all young people being treated in this way to let their Trading Standards Departments know.[9/8]

Part-time working is common in fast food stores, and staff turnover is usually high. In one study[9/1] it was found that a third of those that left fast food employment had been sacked. Yet the law does not permit anyone with less than two years' continuous service to claim for unfair dismissal (unless it is for racial or sexual discrimination). If the job averages less than 16 hours per week then you must work for five years to gain the right to claim. Effectively very few people in fast food service ever earn this basic employment right.

Discrimination

It is notoriously difficult to prove that racist or sexist practices are operating in a place of work. Furthermore, the barriers to getting these practices properly exposed in an industrial tribunal or court of law deter most workers from complaining about what they experience. Only very rarely do clear-cut cases of discrimination get publicity in the press.

In one of the longest race discrimination industrial tribunals ever heard, lasting 22 days, Pizzaland was accused of racially discriminating against the Egyptian managers of its central London branches. According to one report, the tribunal heard that senior staff at Pizzaland headquarters plotted "to get rid of those bloody Egyptians" and in less than six months had dismissed three managers and forced a fourth to resign.[9/9] The tribunal accepted that many Egyptians had helped build up the Pizzaland operations in the 1970s, before it was bought by United Biscuits UK Ltd in 1979. In 1984 a new Operations Director was appointed and by the end of 1985 all the Egyptians in management posts had been removed, a total of nine out of 14 staff at their level. Between April and October 1985 nearly half of all disciplinary actions, and

Discrimination against ethnic minorities in employment can happen in different ways. Sometimes employers just don't want black people in their workforce and find reasons to sack them or not take them on in the first place. Employers can also make black employees want to leave by direct racial harassment, or in less obvious ways, by always finding reasons to refuse promotion or better pay. Employers often rely on the likelihood that ethnic minority workers will not complain because of language difficulties or a sense of isolation or a lack of awareness about their rights. (*Restora*, May 1987)[9/12]

over 80% of the dismissals in London were of Arabs, though they made up less than 15% of the workforce.

The company was found guilty of racial discrimination. Three of the dismissed managers were awarded record amounts in compensation, ranging from £14,812 to £17,708. Two other Egyptian staff were also awarded £6,000 each.[9/10]

A major lesson from the successful tribunal case is that black workers should not have much faith in written equal opportunities policies. Pizzaland's personnel director says his company is an equal opportunities employer and that "We're very confident that this sort of thing will not happen again."[9/11] As *Restora*, the Bangalee restaurant workers' journal points out, the case was exposed "only because the four Egyptians took their case to the tribunal and insisted that the real reason they were sacked was because they were Egyptian, not because of the excuses given by the company".

Due to high unemployment levels among black school-leavers, they represent a disproportionately large pool of available labour, often willing to accept the pay levels and unsocial hours generally prevalent in the catering industry. "We don't look at people's colour or nationality" said one manager, "but their availability."[9/13]

Hazards

"When you are busy, you don't wait for the buns and burgers until they are ready. With the fries, you switch off the fryer while they are still frying, so the buzzer won't go off, after you've taken them out. I would go so far as to say that managers do it too; many will keep fries for longer than the regulation time. If they are short of staff and the queues are growing, they will turn a blind eye whatever you do, provided that you keep going."[9/14]

Recent estimates indicate that over 150 serious accidents are reported in the catering industry each year, along with several thousands of accidents and injuries which never get formally reported. New regulations will require management to report any injuries resulting from accidents which lead to over three days off work, but many accidents never get recorded in the accident book and workers can feel reluctant to make accident claims, or encourage their management to eliminate the risks, because they "don't want to cause trouble".[9/15]

The very nature of fast food preparation – fast! – must put workers on the food preparation line under pressure to work quickly to tight schedules. This can lead to problems with taking time to complete each task properly, taking trouble to clean up any spillage, keeping the work area tidy and well-organised and keeping records of any accidents or near-misses.

Even the best-designed kitchen, carefully designed procedures and well-intentioned company policies cannot withstand the pressure of "just-in-time" frenetic production. The reality in various kitchens can be harsh.

"The kitchen is very hot and the atmosphere even worse without proper air-conditioning. People often have nosebleeds and their skins are getting sore. The kitchen is also very dangerous, especially the fries station, because the floor is very slippery, covered with little drops of oil."[9/16]

"Working there is not a safe place. You can get burned very easily. One time I got burnt by the grill. It was kept at 350°F. The manager on seeing my burn told me to work harder because there would be lots of times when I would get burnt like that. He walked away with a smile on his face. I was angry and lost my temper. All my friends told me to cool down. The meat on the grill was burning. A floor manager told me to go take a drink and relax for five minutes."[9/17]

Recent changes in benefit regulations have removed a worker's right to claim disablement benefit for "small" injuries, leading to less than 14% disablement. Many relatively "minor" injuries occur in catering – cuts, loss of fingers, back injuries – for which, now, there may be no statutory benefits.

One characteristic of modern fast food production that distinguishes it from the general catering industry is its bright, clean surfaces and kitchens often visible to the public. But cleanliness involves chemicals and these can be hazardous to employees. And even some of the most modern machinery can be dangerous.

Here is a quick checklist of some of the hazards which fast food workers might face.[9/18]

Chemicals

Ammonia: present in several cleaning agents, it is also an irritant like bleach, and may lead to headaches, insomnia and disturbed vision.

Bleach: used for cleaning down surfaces, basins and toilets, it is an eye, nose, throat and lung irritant and corrosive. When heated or in contact with acid it releases poisonous chlorine gases.

Caustic Soda: present in some cleaning agents and used on its own to unblock sinks and drains, it can burn the skin and its fumes irritate the nose and throat.

Chlorine: present in some disinfectants and lavatory cleaners, it is an irritant, it can burn skin, and it can kill.

Detergents: can dry out and irritate the skin, and in some individuals cause dermatitis.

Dustbin cleaners: may contain hazardous chemicals.

Pesticides: used to control pests and vermin in kitchens etc., these are dangerous chemicals and may poison and even kill humans.

Solvents: these may be used for certain types of cleaning, e.g. carpets, and may cause headaches, nausea, and possibly lead to kidney and liver damage. Solvents may easily catch fire.

Sulphuric Acid: used to unblock sinks and drains, it can burn the skin and give off acid fumes affecting the eye, nose and throat.

Asbestos: used extensively in buildings and some kitchen equipment to insulate from heat and act as a fire break, small particles of asbestos dust can lead to lung and stomach diseases which eventually kill.

Equipment

Chip cutters: both reciprocating and rotary chip cutters have fast-moving blades.

Knives and other sharp implements: apart from obvious handling accidents, additional hazards occur when handles are left greasy, or when sharp edges are mixed with other implements for washing-up.

Walk-in cold stores: these can trap staff, and should have interior door handles, and back-up lighting if there is a power failure.

Ovens and hot-plates: these frequently cause burns to staff.

Microwaves: surveys have found that significant numbers of these ovens continue to show leakage of the microwave radiation despite improved design features.

Deep fat fryers: these are well-known in the catering industry as being the source of severe burns and scalds, as they are operated at temperatures approaching 200°C, twice the temperature of boiling water.

Fire is a major risk in virtually any enterprise, and catering provides many potential sources of fire. The *Catering Times*[9/19] estimates that there are six restaurant fires *every day* in the UK, a quarter of them due to electrical faults, and nearly three-quarters due to burning fat and grease flare-ups.

To show that they have taken reasonable precautions to prevent a fire, a Fire Certificate needs to be obtained by all the larger establishments, i.e. those places where either 20 people work at any one time, or 10 people work elsewhere than on the ground floor at any one time. If the business is smaller than this then no Fire Certificate is needed and so no inspection is required.

Other hazards to be aware of, and which apply in the catering industry as much as anywhere, include poor lighting levels, high noise levels, poor ventilation, high temperatures, secondary smoking, and the stresses which result from long hours, shiftworking and various forms of harassment.

Turning to the union

"We have no say whatever. Everything is on a take-it-or-leave-it basis. You don't like it, you move out... It is difficult to be represented with this labour turnover but of course I would join a union if there was one..."[9/20]

In a study by Yiannis Gabriel, only 10% of the fast food staff he interviewed had worked at the same place for as long as two years.[9/21] Job security appeared to be of little concern, with the priority being to earn money and have good workmates. They had little hope of promotion, and believed that fast food offered "crap jobs". Struggling for better pay was not a key issue, it appeared, but as the majority of those interviewed lived at home with their parents, they were trapped in a youth pay rate which could not buy independence from home. As one union officer said, "These comments on workers' priorities are useful for any union wishing to develop a recruitment strategy in fast food chains. Despite the high turnover, the poor working conditions can provide the basis for unionisation."[9/22]

In Gabriel's study 70% of the fast food workers he interviewed in a major chain agreed that they needed union protection and help over pay and conditions. They felt the union could give them a voice where they had none at present.

In contrast, senior management can have a very different view of their company and their employees. McDonald's UK President, Paul Preston, interviewed in the *Financial Times* described unions as unnecessary in this form of working relationship. "It is a different sort of thinking, and if trade unions ever started to spread within McDonald's we would see it in our results and our sales."[9/23]

Although trades unions have failed to gain a foothold in the UK McDonald's outlets, they have succeeded in other countries, particularly where basic employment protection rights for individual workers are relatively strong. In Sweden trade unions are reported to have won the right to visit McDonald's outlets, inform workers of their rights and recruit members. In Dublin, McDonald's workers have recently won union rights, and in Mexico a three-week picket is reported to have won the union full recognition with holiday, sick pay and paternity leave rights. And in Nicaragua (yes – McDonald's in Nicaragua!) it is reported that the union not only has sole negotiating rights, but paid time off for union reps and 90 days' paid leave for each worker to attend educational programmes.[9/24]

McDonald's happens to be the best-documented of the fast food chains when it comes to issues of international labour relations, but it should not be assumed that they stand alone in their attitudes towards unionisation. Many large UK and multinational companies are not unionised and their workers may well be content. But in the catering industry, with its transient labour force, unions have the potential to offer greater employee continuity and collective power.

As consumers wanting to change the food being offered to us we may feel overwhelmed by the might of the large and remote companies, whose attitude seems to be: here are our products – take them or leave them. Workers face a similar frustration in their aspirations for better employment: this is the job – take it or leave it. In both cases the individual may want to challenge the authority of the senior management of the company. But such challenges may only be successful if the individuals join together and mount their challenge collectively.

Collectively, as workers, things can be made to change, as the examples of successful struggles overseas show. For more details on trade union rights, health and safety at work and employment rights, contact the catering sections of the following trade unions (addresses are given at the back of this book): Transport and General Workers' Union; GMB; Union of Shop, Distributive and Allied Workers; and the National Union of Railworkers.

Collectively, as consumers, things can also be made to change although there are no ready-made organisations designed to take on these battles. The next chapter will look at what a motivated customer can do practically.

Chapter 10 What you can do

A keen health advocate may try to convince you that all fast food is junk. But people with just a half-hour break for lunch, or caring for children, or with little chance to cook or who simply want something hot to eat, know that they are not going to die from eating the occasional double burger and fries.

At the same time many people feel that fast foods do not rate highly on the health scales. This book has shown in some detail that such feelings are justified. People suspect that the quality of the food may not be as good as it could be, and that the food may be loaded with unexpected ingredients and hidden additivies. Again, this book gives some weight to those suspicions.

Parents of young children may not be too pleased by the way fast foods are advertised and promoted to their children. Food is turned into entertainment, parents may feel, with little concern being given for the long-term consequences. Local residents may feel threatened by the advent of a fast food store in their street, with the accompanying fear of late-night noise and disturbance along with a fear of unacceptable amounts of empty cartons and half-eaten food. And anyone concerned for the wider environmental issues such as the destruction of Costa Rican rainforest, the destruction of the ozone layer or the "hamburgerisation" of countries' diets and their economies, may feel they can no longer sit by and wait for something to be done.

Taking steps

But what can be done? What action can you take to get changes made? Certainly, you can act as an individual, making individual choices. Much of this book is devoted to giving just the sort of information that can help you make such choices between fast food products. Slowly, the choice of items that people go for will get reflected in company sales sheets, and the companies might start to take notice. Public demand, it is said, created the salad bars that

McDonald's now offers in many countries in the world, though not in the UK.

But voting with your wallet is a very slow and inefficient way of communicating with the senior decision-makers in the larger companies, the faceless few who make the decisions affecting the day-to-day content of what you are sold and what you could be sold. Better by far to speak to them directly. Producing this book is one means, of course, as it will eventually get onto the shelves of the company libraries and research departments. But more needs to be done if consumers are to get what they want.

Firstly it is important to sort out exactly what *is* wanted. It needs to be made clear that consumers are not happy with some of their practices and want to see changes. Here is a suggested Consumers' Chart to be used in putting pressure on the decision-makers, both those in the companies and those on the government committees which draw up the regulations governing company activities.

Fast food Consumers' Charter

- We have a right to know what the food consists of nutritionally
- We have a right to know what ingredients have been put in the food
- We have a right to know the origin of the ingredients put in the food and the materials used in the production of the food, so that we may avoid those which we believe may be environmentally damaging
- We have a right to know company policy on employment so that we may avoid those places with whose policies we disagree.

On the basis of a charter such as this, a concerted effort can be made to get the information out of food companies and to let them know what you think of their products.

Telling them what you want

Writing letters and making telephone calls to fast food companies can be very effective. Fast food companies are sensitive about their image. Furthermore, a company that does not want to change may well feel defensive about its products. But a company that has an eye to the future may actually welcome criticism and complaints, as from these they can spot new markets and the potential for new products. Consumers' voices are the source of many a good idea for company bosses, and in this sense you have to feed them with what you want them to feed you. Don't want ozone-damaging boxes? Say so. Don't want beef fat in your french fries? Say so.

During National Consumers' Week in 1985, President Reagan made the following statement:[10/1]

"To make responsible decisions in our dynamic and abundant economy, consumers need both information and education if they are to reap the full benefits of the market-place. They need information, the facts about goods and services: they need to be educated so they can analyze those facts before making a purchase. This will enable them to make wise choices whether they are shopping for food, shelter, clothing, transportation, recreation, health care, entertainment, and so on. Prudent, informed, discriminating consumers put pressure on suppliers to keep improving products and services while devising production efficiencies that will permit them to keep their prices competitive."

To help make your needs known, we have included at the back of this book a list of the addresses of the main companies responsible for the fast food chains in Britain. Even though there are more small, independent fast food outlets than there are outlets belonging to the big chains, the big chains have more clout to get things done about the quality and nature of fast food nowadays and in the future as the dominance of the fast food chains grows. One person in a large company is likely to have more effect than 10 individual take-away managers. Even the large company can feel sensitive about its public image. At the same time, it is well worth pursuing changes at your local fish-and-chip shop or sandwich bar as they will be sensitive to losing local trade. Just getting your local store to make changes can demonstrate that *it can be done.*

It is the London Food Commission's experience - and many other consumer groups' too - that writing letters can have an influence, especially if copies are sent to legislators, such as local councillors and MPs, and to consumer groups. We have included some addresses for doing this at the back of the book.

Which companies are more forthcoming?

In early 1988, the London Food Commission wrote to a dozen of the leading fast food chains in Britain, asking the companies for a statement of their policies on fast food quality. We asked:

"Does your company have a policy on nutritional quality? Does it have a policy on food additives? Do you publish ingredient

lists or are lists available to the public? Does your company plan to provide nutritional and ingredient information to customers?"

Only two companies took the trouble to answer in detail. One, Wimpy, had already sent us the most details on the ingredient and nutritional listings of any company, and they gave us the following answers (in summary):

"We aim to provide good, popular food served quickly whilst also offering good value for money. We continuously examine products to improve quality and value for money, with a view to ensuring that every ingredient fulfils a purpose in the quality/value for money objectives. Wimpy is planning to display leaflets in a test situation. In the meantime, this material and further information is available on request." Wimpy (28.1.88)

And Pizzaland, a branch of United Biscuits along with Wimpy, also took the trouble to write a reply. In summary this said:

"We have a nutritional policy to attempt to eliminate additives where possible. We do not publish ingredients' lists but would release details of ingredients and food additives to members of the public on request. We are not planning to display ingredient information in our outlets at present." Pizzaland (5.2.88)

Besides these two replies, the London Food Commission received no other explicit answers to its requests. In 1987 the Food Commission asked for information on ingredients and nutrients from the very same companies. At the same time we arranged for consumers independent of the Food Commission to write asking for the same information from these same companies.

Our survey found:

- PepsiCo (Pizza Hut, Taco Bell) would not give the London Food Commission the requested nutritional information, claiming that their US data was not "directly relevant" to their UK products. But they supplied one of our consumer sleuths with a list of some of the additives and ingredients to be found in their pizzas, although they would not supply a complete ingredient listing.
- McDonald's can supply their nutritional tables to people who ask, but will not release their ingredients' lists. They were prepared to give the London Food Commission details of some additives to be found in some of their products, but to our independent consumers they wrote saying they would investigate their queries. At the time of going to press (over 10

months later) nothing further had been heard. In the USA, though, things are rather different. McDonald's and several other large chains all provide *both nutrition and ingredient brochures* at all of their outlets to the public.

- Pizza Express told us they wouldn't give out information about their recipes for, among "many reasons", the fact that they have franchised restaurants, where their food preparation manual is kept in "absolute privacy". They told one of our independent consumers that they did not have the time to find out the requested details.
- Burger King sent us their US nutrition and ingredient guide, but asked us to note that the speciality sandwiches, fries, drinks and breakfasts in the UK differed in ingredients and should not be relied upon. Our independent consumers received the same useful leaflet, which includes sample meals as well as item by item listings and even a diabetic exchange list, but received no warning about the data being inappropriate for the UK.
- Trust House Forte (Happy Eater, Little Chef, etc.) did not wish to send us anything. But they also run Kentucky Fried Chicken in this country from separate headquarters and Kentucky did send us some sample ingredient listings and a nutrition table, although they did not reply to our independent consumer.
- Spud-U-Like, owned by the British School of Motoring, sent us their leaflet which includes fibre and calorie information but no details of additives.

This is just a sample selection of the sort of information you may, or may not, get when you write a polite letter. One company would not give any useful details about their products and became very defensive when they thought we would state here that they had refused to co-operate. In contrast, perhaps the most forthcoming was Wimpy, along with the detailed leaflet from Burger King. These are companies that we should hold up to those others who claim that they have to maintain "commercial confidentiality."

Commercial confidentiality is a non-starter as an excuse. Anyone in the fast food trade can find out what is in a product and produce a look-alike if they wish. Many companies buy from the same suppliers and senior staff are moving from one company to another all the time. Really, the only secrets that companies can keep are the details which might affect *you* when you choose your food. They aren't too keen to tell you which foods are high in beef fat or loaded with salt or dosed with sodium benzoate or butylated hydroxytoluene. They know that if you find out too much about the ingredients you might think twice about ordering the product.

Brick walls

Under present UK regulations, companies are not obliged to reveal what the ingredients of their products are nor state their nutritional composition. We may feel we have a natural right to know but in law we have no such right.

Part of the struggle, then, must be to put pressure on law-makers to get the regulations changed and make informative labelling a requirement of fast food retailing. This means putting pressure on government ministries, notably the Department of Health which formulates health policy, and the Ministry of Agriculture, Fisheries and Food (MAFF) which regulates the food industry.

One problem with bureaucracies, especially those in large ministries, is that they are very skilled at writing letters which do not really help you. Here are 10 types of answer which they might use to put you off complaining:

1. "The issues you raise are not the concern of this Department."
2. "Thank you for your letter. We shall look into the matter in due course..."
3. "The Ministry considered this issue last year as part of its review of the 1984 Food Act. Its findings will be published at a time yet to be determined."
4. "The Minister has instructed me to write to you to explain that we cannot at present undertake to respond to letters received from individual members of the public."
5. "We have received no complaints about the matter you raise."
6. "We are unable at present to allocate any resources to an investigation of the issues you raise."
7. "The changes you are suggesting have been tried but met with no success."
8. "This is a matter for individual choice and not for government legislation."
9. "The products you complain of are sold in large numbers and so clearly fulfil a need."
10. "There is no scientific evidence that a significant problem exists."

Behind these off-putting replies is a large and complex web of government departments, politicians, advisory committees and vested commercial interests. One recent book on the workings of government machinery relating to food regulations found that many of the official government advisory committees were stacked with senior staff from the food companies, with hardly any consumer representation.[10/2]

The author of that book, Geoffrey Cannon, looked at 19 government committees spanning the years 1974 to 1987 and found that over half the seats on those committees were occupied by food industry employees, industry-funded academics or members of the industry-funded British Nutrition Foundation. Such industry interests have a right to be heard, of course, but should they have a vote on these decision-making bodies? Should they have over 30 votes? The companies making or selling fast foods were there among the others, as we show in Table 10.1.

Table 10.1 **Some food companies with staff on government committees**

Official government advisory committees 1974–1987	*people*	*committees*
Allied Lyons (Baskin Robbins, etc.)	1	1
Associated British Foods (baked goods, ingredients)	1	3
Grand Metropolitan (Berni's, Barnaby's)	2	5
Ranks Hovis McDougall (Crispins, Sarah's, ingredients)	4	5
Reckitt & Colman (soft drinks, sauces, condiments)	2	4
Scot Bowyers (meat products)	1	1
Unilever (fats & oils, meat products, etc.)	12	20
United Biscuits (Wimpy, Pizzaland, etc.)	1	1
Whitbread (Pizza Hut, Wendy's UK, TGI Friday)	3	3

source: 11.2

Food company representatives also sit on the Wages Councils which, despite their weakened powers since the 1986 Wages Act, are still charged with defining the statutory minimum wages in the fast food outlets.

In the face of such an array of corporate power, it is little wonder that government decisions tend to put the consumer second to the needs of industry. Our foods do not have the sort of compositional labelling that we expect on our clothes, and our fast food has no useful labelling at all. Food standards are to be replaced by manufacturers' declarations, yet there are no declarations at all on fast foods. We are encouraged to eat healthily and choose foods with a lower fat content, but there is no fat labelling on fast foods to give us the choice we need.

No fat labelling yet, at least. There are, though, suggestions that fat could be declared, even on fast foods. A DHSS advisory committee on preventing heart disease did come up with the recommendation in 1984 that the fat content of foods should be clearly labelled. Three years later the Ministry of Agriculture drafted some suggestions for the nutritional labelling of foods, including catering foods, but these have not yet been made compulsory. The Ministry came up with guidelines for labelling catering foods which have been circulated to interested parties to see how well the ideas go down. To date, no firm indication of what, or when, legislation and implementation of the guidelines will be introduced.

Caterers are, according to the 1987 "preliminary draft" guidelines, encouraged to show what the fat content of their meals is, either in grams or as a percentage weight (possibly in the form of grams of fat per 100gm of dinner). Alternatively, caterers could "highlight in some way those foods sold which will enable a customer to keep a sensible fat intake." Or they may prefer to mention on the menu that advice from "highly trained personnel" is available for the asking. Or they may group lower-fat foods together in a display and put up a notice identifying them.

We are not sure that these will prove very helpful. To give details of fat as percentage of the weight could be quite misleading: a mixture of fat and water (such as a low-sugar milk-shake) may be only 5% fat in weight, but over 90% in the calories it gives you. It is the fat as a percentage of the calories which you need to be concerned about. The original DHSS report recommended a national average of fat in the diet to be no higher than 35% *of the calories*, not of the weight of food. French fries might have 13 to 14% fat by weight, but have nearer 40 to 45% fat as a proportion of the calories they supply.

Getting to grips

What is needed to overcome these stubborn but powerful interests? First, we need well-informed consumers, able to see when they are being duped. This book is designed to help consumers become better informed and better able to act.

Second, we need to know who to lobby and to whom to complain. We need to know where the power to change things lies and how best to influence that power in our interests. Again, we have tried in this book to give a little of the insight needed to see where the power and control really lie. And we have included a section at the end on addresses to contact: addresses of agencies that can offer support and agencies that need to be complained to as well as the addresses of the companies themselves.

Third, we need to recruit effective advocates. We need people who can act on our behalf and stand up for what we want. Consumer organisations set themselves up to perform this role and we have included the relevant ones in the address lists.

Fast food: *don't just swallow it!*

If fast food is the food of the future, then we all need to do all that we can to ensure it is *good* food. Ask for the information. Write to the companies. Make your voice heard and don't just swallow what they sell you!

References and sources

Sources of information referred to in the book

0'1 Statement from Peggy Fenner, then Parliamentary Secretary of the Ministry of Agriculture Fisheries and Food, published in *Fair Trader*, February 1986, and re-issued as a press release from the Ministry under the name of Michael Jopling, Minister of Agriculture, during 1987.

0'2 Proclamation made by President Ronald Reagan, December 1985, in honour of National Consumers' Week, cited in *The Fast Food Guide* by M F Jacobson and S Fritschner, Workman Publishing, New York 1986.

0'3 Cover review quoting Robin Murray, ex-Chief Economic Advisor, Greater London Council.

1'1 *London Restaurant Business*, 14 December 1987.

1'2 Evidence submitted by the company to the Department of Environment for planning application appeal.

1'3 "Dietary habits of 15 to 25-year olds" by N Bull, Supplement 1 to *Human Nutrition: Applied Nutrition* 39a, 1985, pp. 1–68.

1'4 Report on St Aloysius School project by Islington Health Authority Health Education Department, 1987.

1'5 Euromonitor Survey, 1986

1'6 London Food Commission survey of fast food eaters *Grazing in Peckam* by F Carruthers, 1988, cited in *Food Magazine*, No 1, 1988.

2'1 Food regulations, cited in *The Meat Machine* by J Walsh, Columbus Books, London 1986.

2'2 *The Meat Machine op. cit.*

2'3 London Food Commission data. The list is similar (but extended) to that given by M Hanssen's *E for Additives Supermarket Shopping Guide*, Thorsons, London 1986.

3'1 Figures for average calories burnt per minute of activity taken from *Exercise Physiology* by Brooks and Fahel, Collier McMillan, 1987, and *Human Nutrition and Dietetics* by R Passmore and M A Eastwood, Churchill Livingstone (Longman), London 1986.

4'1 J M Pascoe, J Dockerty and J Ryley, Chapter 5, Fast Foods, in *Nutrition in Catering* (Richard Cottrell ed) Proceedings of the Seventh British Nutrition Foundation Annual Conference, Parthenon Publishing Group: Carnforth, Lancs, 1987.

5'1 M Nelson and D Naismith, 1979, cited in *Tightening Belts*, by I Cole-Hamilton and T Lang, London Food Commission, 1986.

5'2 Hackett *et al.*, 1984, cited in *Tightening Belts*, *op. cit.*

5'3 K M Goel, 1979, and M Blaxter and E Paterson, 1983, cited in *Tightening Belts*, *op. cit.*

5′4 MAFF, 1985, cited in *Tightening Belts, op. cit.*

5′5 N Bull, 1985, and J Bourne, 1985, cited in *Tightening Belts, op. cit.*

5′6 W. Doyle, 1982, and M Crawford *et al.*, 1986, cited in *Tightening Belts, op. cit.*

5′7 *The Diets of British School-children – Preliminary Report of a Nutritional Analysis of a nationwide dietary survey of British School-children* by R Wenlock *et al.*, Department of Health and Social Security, 1986.

5′8 O.P.C.S. *Monitor* and *Inequalities in Health* by P Townsend and N Davidson, Penguin 1982, and *The Health Divide* by M Whitehead, Health Education Council, 1987, and *Tightening Belts, op. cit.*, and *General Household Survey 1985*, O.P.C.S.

5′9 "Takeaway Diet leads to Underweight Babies" by G Vines, *New Scientist*, 25.12.86–1.1.87, and reference *5′6* above.

5′10 See reference *5′7* above.

5′11 *National Advisory Committee on Nutrition Education (NACNE) Report*, Health Education Council, 1983, and *Diet and Cardiovascular Disease*, Report on Health and Social Subjects No. 28, DHSS, H.M.S.O., 1984.

5′12 *Obesity*, Royal College of Physicians, 1983, and *World Health Statistics Annual 1986*, World Health Organisation, 1986, and *The Causes of Cancer* by R Doll and R Peto, Oxford Medical Publications, 1981, and O.P.C.S. *Monitor* SS 83/2, and *Nutrition and Health in Old Age*, DHSS, H.M.S.O., 1979.

5′13 *Diet and Cardiovascular Disease, op. cit.*, and O.P.C.S. Cancer Mortality registrations.

5′14 *Consumer Catering Report*, HOTAG, 1986.

5′15 *Take-away and Eating Out at Restaurants*, Gordon Simmonds Research Ltd, 1987.

5′16 See reference *5′7*.

5′17 See reference *1′3*.

6′1 S Luxembourg, *Roadside Empires*, Viking, cited in *The Fast Food Guide*, op. cit.

6′2 *The Fast Food Guide, op. cit.*

6′3 *Caterer and Hotelkeeper*, October 29th 1987.

6′4 *Caterer and Hotelkeeper*, December 31st 1987.

6′5 Ronald McDonald House Charity promotional literature.

6′6 *Meat Industry*, April 1987.

6′7 *Media and Marketing*, April 15th 1985.

6′8 *The Fast Food Guide, op. cit.*

6′9 New Jersey McDonald's manager, reported in the *Wall Street Journal* and cited in *The Fast Food Guide, op. cit.*

7′1 *Blueprint for a Green Planet*, by J Seymour and H Girardet, Dorling Kindersley, London 1987.

7′2 Data sources include *Retail Business*, 337, March 1986.

7′3 See reference *5′15*.

7′4 Industry data, also *Sunday Times Business Supplement* feature, August 12th 1984, and *Working for Big Mac*,Transnationals Information Centre, London 1987.

7′5 Sources include Company Reports, *The Food Trades Directory 1987–88*, Newman Books, London 1987, and *Popular Foodservice*, December 1986, and *Working for Big Mac, op. cit.*

7′6 Sources as for *7′5* and also *London Restaurant Business*, January 18th 1988.

7'7 *Working for Big Mac*, *op. cit.*

7'8 *Wimpy International Limited Company Profile*, by Daniel J Edelman Ltd, London, March 1986.

7'9 *Retail Business*, 337, March 1986, and *Everybody's Business: an Almanac* by M Moskowitz *et al.*, San Francisco 1980 (cited in IBON Facts and Figures, *The Fast Money-Makers*, January 31st 1984, IBON Databank, Manila 1984).

7'10 *Retail Business*, *op. cit.*

7'11 See reference *7'10*.

7'12 McDonald's *Annual Report 1986*.

7'13 See reference *7'12*.

7'14 See reference *7'12*.

7'15 Letter from KFC, and *Popular Foodservice*, November 1987.

7'16 IBON Facts and Figures (*op. cit* reference 7'9).

7'17 "Hit by Fast Food Fever" by P Pillai and F Chong, *Malay Mail*, April 22nd 1982.

7'18 "Comparative Study of Fast Food Chains in Singapore" by W C Hou and W R Swinyard, *Singapore Management Review*, 8, January 1986, citing *The Straits Times* of October 1985.

7'19 "McDonald's All Set for the Big Day", Bangkok *Sunday Nation*, November 17th 1984.

7'20 "Of Blondes, Burgers and Japanese" by P Massey, New York *Star*, February 4th 1986.

7'21 See reference *7'20*.

7'22 "McHeartbreak" by L Goodman-Malamuth, *Nutrition Action*, 13, January 1986.

7'23 "The Fast Food Phenomenon" by P W Smith, *Asia Magazine*, January 15th 1984.

7'24 "Consumers and Street Foods" by A Allain, IOCU consultant, prepared for *FAO Workshop on Street Foods in Asia*, Indonesia, November 3rd–7th 1986.

7'25 See reference *7'19*.

7'26 "Poor British spud has had its chips" by C Wright, *Daily Telegraph*, February 25th 1986.

7'27 See reference *7'1*.

7'28 See reference *7'1*.

7'29 Correspondence from McDonald's (UK), December 12th 1986.

7'30 "Factory Farm 1987", leaflet produced by Compassion in World Farming, Petersfield, 1987.

7'31 Correspondence from Burger King Corporation (USA), February 6th 1987.

7'32 Daniel J Edelman Ltd, Public Relations for Wimpy International, *Wimpy International – A British Success Story* (sheet 1616c), undated but circa 1986.

7'33 McDonald's *Annual Report 1986*.

7'34 "Big Mac Box 'A Threat to Ozone'" by T Moore, *Sunday Times*, March 8th 1987.

7'35 "How to Save the Ozone Layer" by G Lean, *Observer*, September 20th 1987.

8'1 "Surprise in Store", Advertising Feature, *Evening Standard*, November 9th 1987.

8'2 "Consumers spark US food revolution", *Meat Industry*, January 1987.

8'3 "American Special", *Caterer and Hotelkeeper*, October 29th 1987.

8'4 See reference *8'3*.

8'5 "Gulping Down the Future", *London Food News*, 7, London Food Commission, 1987.

8'6 "The Bite that Excites", by M Harris, *Daily Telegraph*, November 10th 1987.

8'7 "Finessing Fat" by E Blume, *Nutrition Action*, November 1987.

8'8 See reference *8'7*.

8'9 *Food Adulteration and How to Beat It*, by The London Food Commission, Unwin Hyman, London 1988.

8'10 Ministry of Agriculture, Fisheries and Food, 1985, cited in *Food Adulteration and How to Beat It, op. cit.*

8'11 *Modern Meat* by O Schell, Vintage Books, New York 1985.

8'12 *New Scientist*, October 2nd 1986, cited in *Food Adulteration and How to Beat It, op. cit.*

8'13 "Hygiene Test for Food Handlers?", *Caterer and Hotelkeeper*, December 3rd 1987.

8'14 "Glass in Burger - £1000 damages", *British Food Journal*, March/April 1985.

8'15 "Burger Bar Fined", *British Food Journal*, July/August 1985.

8'16 "Hygiene Offences on Hotdog Stall", *British Food Journal*, May/June 1987.

8'17 "McDonald's Hamburgers Ltd *v* L F Windle", Queen's Bench Division of the High Court, October 21st 1986, reported in *Fairtrader*, 1, 1987.

9'1 *Working Lives in Catering* by Y Gabriel, Routledge and Kegan Paul, London 1988.

9'2 Williams, *Fortune Magazine*, November 12th 1984, cited in *Working for Big Mac, op. cit.*

9'3 See reference *9'1*.

9'4 Confidential document from ex-fast food worker.

9'5 See reference *9'4*.

9'6 "Counter Culture", Young Observer, *Observer Colour Supplement*, 1986.

9'7 McDonald's *Crew Handbook*, June 1986.

9'8 "Bad Employers Criticised", *Hounslow News Release* No. 63/88, February 5th 1988, and Chief Trading Standards Officer Report to Health and Consumer Protection Committee, Hounslow Council, February 4th 1987.

9'9 "Pizza Prejudice" by J Hughes, *City Limits*, June 18th–25th 1987.

9'10 "Sacked Pizzaland Managers win Record Compensation" by S Guthrie, *London Restaurant Business*, January 25th 1988.

9'11 See reference *9'10*.

9'12 *Restora*, Journal of the Bangalee Restaurant Workers, May 1987.

9'14 *Working Lives in Catering, op. cit.*

9'15 *Risks à la Carte*, Safety Representatives' Guide to Safety Hazards, GMB, Esher 1986.

9'16 Unpublished manuscript quoting fast food interviewees.

9'17 See reference *9'16*.

9'18 Much of this is adapted from *Risks à la Carte, op. cit.*

9'19 *Catering Times*, September 7th 1978.

9'20 See reference *9'14*.

9'21 See reference *9'14*.

9'22 Correspondence with union official, Transport and General Workers' Union, April 1988.

9'23 "Crew system done to a turn" by J Gapper, *Financial Times*, September 14th 1987.

9'24 See reference *9'14*.

10'1 See reference *0'2*.

10'2 *The Politics of Food* by G Cannon, Century, London 1987.

Appendix 1 Nutritional details: the tables

There are, at present, no regulations requiring fast food outlets to label their foods, not even the minimal amounts that appear on products in supermarkets and groceries. Fast food catering is shrouded with secrecy, a secrecy that does nothing to reassure the customer about the quality of the food they are getting.

The quality of food and the quality of information

If you ask at the counter "What's in this stuff?" you may not get a very helpful reply. Catering staff are not given much training in the nutritional content of what they serve, and they are not paid to stand and talk about nutrients.

A few companies have started to print leaflets, though, which give you the news, as they see it, about the product you are buying. We looked at these leaflets in Chapter 6. Apart from these, the only other sources of useful information on the nutritional content of fast foods comes from occasional articles in newspapers and magazines, or from this book.

We have searched all the literature we could find, both from Britain and from countries with similar fast food outlets overseas. And we collaborated with the London Borough of Southwark Public Analyst to have 40 typical fast food items analysed. In the following tables we give you a summary of the details we have accumulated.

Decoding the tables

We have selected those nutrients which are relevant to today's dietary guidelines. Where no information is available we have left it blank. Where only a very small amount of the nutrient is likely to be present, just a trace of it, we have put *tr*.

The quantity of each food item is indicated in the "weight" column. This is normally an average serving size. Where we have used tables that gave non-serving data –

such as "per 100gm" - we have indicated this by putting *ns* before the weight.

We have given total fat in grams and as a proportion of the calories, as a way of comparing the proportion the fat contributes to the total calorie count. We have indicated the amount of fat that is saturated fat.

Checking for health

To help pick out the good features we have underlined figures which indicate that the food provides a rich and useful source of an essential dietary component, defined as follows:

- for *fibre* that it provides at least 20% of average daily needs (i.e. 6gm) and there is at least 1gm per 100 Calories;
- for *iron* that it provides at least 20% of average daily needs (i.e. 3mg) and there is at least 1mg per 100 Calories;
- for *calcium* that it provides at least 20% of average daily needs of pregnant women (i.e. 250mg) and there is at least 50mg per 100 Calories;
- for *vitamin A* that it provides at least 20% of average daily needs (i.e. about 150ug) and there is at least 70ug per 100 Calories;
- for *vitamin C* that it provides at least 20% of average daily needs (i.e. 6mg) and there is at least 2mg per 100 Calories.

In contrast we have circled with square brackets - [...] - figures which indicate a possible hazard to health if the food item forms a substantial part of a regular diet, which we have defined as follows:

- for *fat:* that the fat contributes at least 40% of the calories in the food item, and the food item contributes at least 500 Calories in all;
- for *saturated fat:* that the saturated fat is at least 40% of the total fat, or contributes over 20% of the calories in the food item;
- and for *sodium:* that the quantity of sodium in the food item is at least 0.8gm, equivalent to 2gm of salt.

Company/Product	*Wt.(g)*	*Cals*	*Fat(g)*	*Sat.fat(g)*	*Fat % cals*
Independents					
Cod and chips	477	1054	[56]	9	48%
Chicken and chips	309	890	[55]	18	56%
Doner kebab & salad	265	745	[49]	[25]	59%
Pie, mash & liquor	832	599	16	[8]	24%
Sweet & sour chicken with egg fried rice	912	2052	[106]	9	46%
Cheese & tomato thin crust pizza	246	613	14	[8]	20%
Saveloy and chips	407	794	[42]	9	48%
Fishcake	78	202	11	2	49%
Cod roe in batter	94	162	9	1	52%
Sausage in batter	166	410	24	8	53%
Large beef salad roll	185	350	7	[3]	18%
Cheese salad roll	171	344	12	[7]	33%
Beef chow mein	408	571	[28]	2	44%
Spare ribs in sauce	325	832	[59]	[22]	64%
Spring roll	193	421	26	3	55%
Steak & kidney pie	153	461	29	[16]	56%
Deep fried chicken	149	390	26	8	59%
Jacket potato with cheese & onion	281	461	31	[19]	60%
Onion bhajis	118	355	24	2	60%
Chicken Madras	339	431	25	4	52%
Pilau rice	241	388	3	1	8%
Large shish kebab with salad	370	485	16	6	30%
Cheese & cucumber sandwich (brown)	140	328	14	[7]	38%
Cheese and tomato sandwich (white)	145	334	15	[8]	40%
Cornish pasty	152	523	[33]	10	56%
Cheese & onion pasty	117	358	21	[12]	54%
Sausage roll	75	297	19	6	57%
Fried egg in roll	104	276	12	3	39%
Fried bacon in roll	79	245	10	3	36%
Jamaican patty	138	454	26	[13]	53%
Lamb curry	314	512	[33]	6	58%
Baked potato with chili filling (vegetarian)	613	472	12	4	23%
Big Frank (microwaved)	188	374	16	6	38%
Beefburger in sesame bun (microwaved)	210	504	21	[11]	37%
Fried fish, ackee, rice and peas	609	1230	[71]	16	52%
Chocolate milk shake	153	116	6	[3]	43%
Banana milk shake	136	35	4	[3]	42%

Source: LFC and Southwark Public Protection (Public Analysts)

Sodium(g)	*Fibre(g)*	*Iron(mg)*	*Calcium(mg)*	*Vit.A*	*Vit.C(mg)*
0.2	5	3.3	458		29
[1.5]	3	3.7	130		3
[1.9]	3	3.4	151		tr
[2.9]	8	4.2	300		7
[3.1]	8	8.2	547		18
[2.1]	5	1.7	1028		4
0.7	8	3.3	175		17
0.5	1	0.6	70		1
[0.9]	2	0.7	102		3
[1.8]	2	1.2	174		3
0.7	4	1.3	78		tr
[1.0]	4	0.9	267		tr
[2.4]	4	2.4	155		12
[3.7]	3	0.7	553		26
[1.3]	3	0.8	64		tr
[0.9]	3	1.1	49		tr
0.2	1	1.2	36		tr
[0.9]	3	1.7	975		tr
0.5	5	5.0	83		tr
	6	10.5	193		tr
0.3	1	0.7	70		tr
[1.0]	6	3.7	492		tr
[0.8]	4	0.7	486		tr
0.7	2	0.6	508		tr
[1.0]	2	1.4	169		3
0.7	2	0.6	204		1
0.4	1	0.3	233		1
0.5	2	4.4	74		3
0.7	2	3.3	43		2
[0.8]	2	6.2	94		3
[1.1]	8	13.8	182		tr
[0.8]	18	5.5	257		
[1.3]	2	1.7	100		tr
[1.4]	4	3.6	653		tr
[2.6]	6	3.7	859		tr
0.1	0	0.2	228		tr
0.1	0	1.4	209		tr

Wimpy	*Wt.(g)*	*Cals*	*Fat(g)*	*Sat.fat(g)*	*Fat % cals*
Cheeseburger & chips	263	686	[37]	12	48%
Beanburger in bun & chips	338	926	[53]	8	52%
Hamburger*	106	260	10	[5]	33%
Cheeseburger*	120	305	13	[7]	39%
Kingsize*	201	410	20	[11]	45%
Quarterpounder*	211	540	[29]	[13]	50%
Quarterpounder & cheese*	225	585	[33]	[15]	51%
Halfpounder*	313	830	[54]	[27]	59%
Fish and chips*	213	465	23	3	44%
Chicken in a bun*	180	510	[30]	6	54%
Beanburger & cheese*	236	520	22	6	38%
Chips*	100	275	14	2	44%
Sweets					
Apple pie*	175	315	13	2	37%
Drinks					
White coffee*	(.2L)	18	1		55%
Tea with milk*	(.2L)	18	1		55%
Shake*	(.4L)	260	7	[4]	23%
Small coke*	(.3L)	100	0	0	0%
Large coke*	(.5L)	170	0	0	0%
Orange juice*	(.2L)	61	0	0	0%

McDonald's					
Quarterpounder with French fries	214	589	[30]	[14]	46%
Hamburger*	103	253	10	[5]	35%
Cheeseburger*	117	301	14	[7]	42%
Big Mac*	207	554	[28]	[10]	45%
Chicken McNuggets* (6)	109	265	14	[7]	49%
Filet-o-Fish*	130	414	26	7	56%
French fries* (regular)	93	290	16	[8]	49%
French fries* (large)	124	386	21	[11]	50%
Sweets					
Apple pie*	91	251	15	[7]	55%
Drinks					
Milk*	313	207	14	[8]	62%
Vanilla shake*	299	356	9	[7]	23%
Chocolate shake*	314	389	11	[8]	25%
Cola* (large)	425	120			
Root beer* (regular)	303	83			
Orange drink* (regular)	319	107			

Source: LFC and Southwark Public Protection (Public Analysts), and * company data

Sodium(g)	*Fibre(g)*	*Iron(mg)*	*Calcium(mg)*	*Vit.A*	*Vit.C(mg)*
0.7	6	2.4	239		8
[0.9]	7	4.1	331		14
0.6	2	0.1	58	0	tr
[0.8]	2	1.2	156	34ug	tr
[1.1]	3	2.4	168	94ug	8
[1.1]	7	2.6	102	38ug	2
[1.3]	7	2.7	200	72ug	2
[2.0]	7	5.1	210	72ug	2
	3	2.4	135	0	4
0.3	2	1.1	92	37ug	2
[1.1]	16	3.8	228	319ug	18
0.3	3	1.0	11	0	4
0.2	2	1.0	43	0	0
0.0	0	0.0	34	11ug	1
0.0	0	0.0	34	11ug	1
0.1	0	0.0	169	98ug	2
tr	0	0.0	10	0	0
tr	0	0.0	15	0	0
tr	0	0.9	17		65
[0.8]	5	4	131		9
0.4		1	69	3ug	
0.6		1	153	47ug	
[0.9]		2	177	32ug	
0.5		1	6	0	
0.6		1	141	21ug	
0.3		1	16		4
0.4		1	21		6
0.1		0	24	0	0
0.1		1	238	125ug	0
0.2		1	524	88ug	1
0.3		2	515	107ug	2
0.0					
0.0					0

Breakfast items	Wt.(g)	Cals	Fat(g)	Sat.fat(g)	Fat % cals
Egg McMuffin*	143	312	14	[7]	40%
Scrambled eggs*	94	150	9	[5]	52%
Sausage pattie*	43	160	14	[6]	77%
Hash brown*	53	150	10	[5]	59%
English muffin with butter & jam*	95	268	6	[3]	21%
Orange juice*	178	90			

Source: LFC and Southwark Public Protection (Public Analysts) , and * company data

Burger King					
Hamburger	109	275	12	[5]	39%
Cheeseburger	120	317	15	[7]	43%
Whopper	265	628	[36]	12	52%
Whopper double cheese	288	711	[43]	[17]	54%
Whopper junior	136	322	17	6	48%
Whaler	190	488	27	6	50%
Chicken specialty	230	688	[40]	8	52%
French fries	74	227	13	[7]	52%
Sweets					
Apple pie	135	305	12	4	35%
Drinks					
Whole milk	244	157	9	[6]	52%
Vanilla shake (med.)	273	321	10	[6]	28%
Chocolate shake (med.)	284	320	12	[7]	34%
Pepsi (regular)	366	159	0	0	0%
Diet pepsi (regular)	366	1	0	0	0%
7 Up (regular)		144	0	0	0%
Orange juice		82	0	0	0%

Source: US company data

Kentucky Fried Chicken					
Fried chicken (edible parts) average piece	84	174	11	[4]	58%
Fried chicken 3 pieces	252	522	[33]	[12]	58%
French fries	115	261	11	3	39%
Barbecue beans	90	105	1	0	10%
Coleslaw (small)	80	103	6	1	50%
Corn on the cob	143	176	3	1	16%

Source: US and UK company data

Sodium(g)	*Fibre(g)*	*Iron(mg)*	*Calcium(mg)*	*Vit.A*	*Vit.C(mg)*
0.7		2	184	123ug	
0.2		2	71	109ug	
0.5		1	6	6ug	
0.3		0	7		0
0.2		1	59	39ug	
0.0		0	17		51
0.5		3	37	45ug	3
0.7		3	102	102ug	3
[0.9]		5	84	203ug	12
[1.2]		5	215	318ug	12
0.5		3	40	89ug	6
0.6		2	46	11ug	0
[1.4]		3	79	38ug	0
0.2		1	0	0	2
0.4		1	0	0	5
0.1		0	290	90ug	4
0.2		0	295	0	0
0.2		2	260	0	0
		0	0	0	0
		0	0	0	0
0.0				14ug	71
0.5		1	33	0	0
[1.5]		2	99	0	0
0.1		1	16	0	3
0.4		1	54		2
0.2		0	29	50ug	19
0.0		1	7	50ug	2

Taco Bell	Wt.(g)	Cals	Fat(g)	Sat.fat(g)	Fat % cals
Beef burrito		466	21		41%
Burrito supreme		457	22		43%
Tostada		179	7		30%
Taco		186	8		39%
Bean burrito		343	12		32%

Source: American Council on Science and Health

Pizza Hut	Wt.(g)	Cals	Fat(g)	Sat.fat(g)	Fat % cals
Thin/crispy cheese pizza (half 13-inch)		680	22		29%
Thin/crispy supreme pizza (half 13-inch)		800	34		38%

Source: American Council on Science and Health

Pizzaland	Wt.(g)	Cals	Fat(g)	Sat.fat(g)	Fat % cals
Wholemeal pizza base	168	383	5.4		13%
Deep-pan pizza cheese & tomato	575	1542	53.0		31%
Traditional pizza cheese & tomato	293	692	21.0		27%
Salad	322	301	16.0		45%

Source: company data

Pizza Express (Calories only available)

Source: company data

Pizzas	
American	930
American hot	930
Capricciosa	890
Fiorentina	750
Four Seasons	900
La Reine	810
Margherita	770
Marinara	700
Mushroom	710
Napoletana	820
Neptune	790
Quattro Formaggi	760
Veneziana	760
Other dishes	
Ham & Egg Pizza Express	710
Mozzarella/tomato salad	1120
Garlic bread	210
Desserts	
Chocolate fudge cake	420
Cassata	300
Bombe	320
Fresh fruit salad	80
Cream (small serving	60
Extras	
Anchovy	50
Cheese	120
Egg	90
Ham	40
Mushrooms	10
Olives	50
Onion	5
Pepperonata	10
Pepperoni sausage	120
Peppers	5
Tuna	90
Drinks	
Tomato juice (8oz)	60
Unsweetened orange (8oz)	80
Coke (10oz)	120
Lemonade (10oz)	70
Milk (10oz)	190

Sodium(g)	Fibre(g)	Iron(mg)	Calcium(mg)	Vit.A	Vit.C(mg)
0.3		5	64	400ug	15
0.4		4	96	550ug	16
0.1		2	152	500ug	tr
0.1		3	96	24ug	tr
0.3		3	80	400ug	4
[1.8]		7	800	300ug	tr
[2.4]		9	640	400ug	5
[1.1]	12				
	14				
	5				
	8				

Baskin-Robbins	*Wt.(g)*	*Cals*	*Fat(g)*	*Sat.fat(g)*	*Fat % cals*
Scoops					
Vanilla	ns100	208	12.0		52%
Praline 'n'cream	ns100	246	12.6		46%
Rocky road	ns100	259	12.2		42%
Jam, almond fudge	ns100	218	11.2		46%
Choc chip/mint	ns100	230	13.7		54%
Lemon sherbet	ns100	144	1.2		8%

Source: company data and LFC estimates

Spud-U-Like	*Wt.*	*Cals*	*Fat(g)*	*Sat.fat(g)*	*Fat % cals*
Baked potato	(10oz)	250	0.0		1%
Baked potato with butter		355			
Tuna salad	(3oz)	340			
Cottage cheese	(3oz)	360	3.0		9%
Cheddar cheese	(3oz)	490	30.0		55%
Baked beans	(4oz)	320			
Chilli con carne	(4oz)	355			
Sweetcorn		340			
Other items (Calories only)					
Chicken soup		95			
Garlic bread		325			
Mini French roll		235			
Soups		70-120			

Source: LFC estimates and company data

Appendix 2 **Ingredients and additives: the details**

In Chapter 2 we indicated the sorts of fast foods likely to contain some of the unexpected, and for some people greatly unwanted, elements which the food industry puts into its products.

In this section we give more detailed listings of foods containing ingredients and additives which people may need or want to avoid, for physical or cultural reasons.

These details are not usually given to the public. The ingredients' lists may, however, be found on the wholesale cartons and we have hunted through cash and carry warehouses, in the fast food restaurant dustbins and at fast food trade fairs and exhibitions to compile the following lists.

Without undertaking extensive chemical analyses we cannot vouch for the accuracy of the information. We can only report what we found on the manufacturers' labels and in their literature. The information we print here represents a fair cross-section of the industry, but there are

Sodium(g)	Fibre(g)	Iron(mg)	Calcium(mg)	Vit.A	Vit.C(mg)
tr	8	2	23	tr	11+
	8				
	9				
0.4	8	2	70	18ug	11+
0.6	8	2	750	200ug	11+
	16	3			
	13	4	60		
	14				

many small companies - and some large ones - whose product ingredients we have not been able to identify. Furthermore, manufacturers and restaurants tend to change their ingredients and their suppliers, so that the fish and chips that had tartrazine in them last week, for example, may now have annatto instead.

De-coding the table

The listings which follow give details of the ingredients which we examined in Chapter 2. These include the presence, or possible presence, of any of the following:

- **Animal products** this means ingredients derived from dead animals, including animal carcass fat (e.g. lard, tallow), glycerine and gelatin, and the meat-derived flavour enhancers (631, 635).
  A *?* indicates the presence of one of the emulsifiers E471-E475 and E481-E495 which can be made from either animal or vegetable fats and the manufacturers have not specified which one they have used.
- **Fish products** this includes the fish-derived flavour enhancers (627, 631).
  A *?* indicates that an ingredient which may include fish is present, such as Worcester Sauce (into which some manufacturers put anchovies).
- **Insect products** this includes the colouring cochineal (E120) and the glaze shellac (904).
- **Milk products** this includes dried milk, skimmed milk

powder, lactose, whey, casein and milk derived additives E270, E325–E327, E472(b) and 478.

- **Egg products** this includes albumin.
- **Wheat products** this includes gluten and bran.
- **Soya products** this includes the emulsifier lecithin (E322), but excludes soya oil.
- **Flavour enhancers** these include the ones referred to above (627–635), the maltols (636 and 637) and the glutamates which may be wheat- or soya-protein derived (620–623).
  An *m* indicates monosodium glutamate (621).
- **Colourants** these include all added colouring agents (E100–180).

Food/Product	*Animal*	*Fish*	*Insect*	*Milk*	*Egg*
Condiments and relishes					
Amoy Dark Soya Sauce					
Amoy Hoi-Sin Sauce					
Caterers Kitchen Brown Sauce					
Caterers Kitchen Tomato Sauce					
Colmans English Mustard					
Costa Soya Sauce					
Encona West Indian Pepper Sauce					
Frank Coopers Burger Relish					
Frank Coopers Horseradish Sauce					
Hammonds Malt Vinegar					
Hammonds Soya Sauce					
Hammonds Tomato Sauce					
Heinz Malt Vinegar					
HP English Mustard					
HP French Mustard					
HP Malt Vinegar					
HP Mint Sauce					
HP Soy Sauce					
HP Tartare Sauce					●
Kraft Brown Sauce					
Kraft Tartare Sauce (bulk)					●
La Victoria Chili Dip					
La Victoria Taco Sauce					
Lea & Perrin Worcestershire Sauce		●			
MCC Country Cottage Tomato Ketchup					
MCC Country Cottage Tartare Sauce					●

A *c* indicates one of the coal-tar or azo dyes.
An *a* indicates annatto.

- **Preservatives** these include all preserving agents (E200–297) and all anti-oxidants (E300–E321).
  A *z* indicates a benzoate.
  An *s* indicates sulphur dioxide or a sulphite.
  A *n* indicates a nitrate or nitrite.
  A *g* indicates a gallate.
  A *B* indicates the presence of BHA or BHT.
- **Artificial sweeteners** these include aspartame, sacharin and acesulfame-k, hydrogenated glucose syrup, isomalt, thaumatin and xylitol.

Wheat	*Soya*	*Flav-En.*	*Colour*	*Pres.*	*Art-Sweet.*
●	●	m	●	●	
●	●		●,c		
●	●		●		●
●			c		●
●			●,c		
	●		●		
				z	
				●	
●	●			B,s	●
			●		
●	●		●	●	
			c	●	●
			●	s	
●					
●			●		
			●		
			c		
	●		●		
				B	
	●				
			●		
				z	
				z	
				●	

Food/Product	*Animal*	*Fish*	*Insect*	*Milk*	*Egg*
Newtons Caribbean Pepper Sauce			●		
Sharwoods Light Soy Sauce					
Sharwoods Pineapple Chutney					
Sharwoods Rich Soy Sauce					
Vinney Non-brewed Condiment					
Burger King Barbecue Sauce*					
Burger King Sweet & Sour Sauce*		?			
Burger King Tartare Sauce*					●
McDonald Mild Mustard Sauce					
McDonald Barbecue Sauce					
McDonald Mac Sauce					
McDonald Tartare Sauce					
Wimpy Ketchup					
Wimpy Special Sauce				●	●
Wimpy White Sauce					●
Other sauces and powder mixes					
Amoy Hoi-Sin Barbecue Sauce					
Amoy Satay Sauce					
Amoy Sweet & Sour Sauce					
Blue Dragon Canton Sauce					
Blue Dragon Szechuan Sauce					
Colmans Curry Sauce Mix				●	
Colmans Sweet & Sour Mix					
Conimex Peanut Sate Mix		●		●	
Costa Spare Rib Sauce					
Crosse & Blackwell Madras Curry Mix					
Gebhardt Taco Sauce					
Golden Pagoda Hoi-Sin BBQ Sauce					
Hammonds Spare Rib Sauce					
Knorr Korma Curry Mix	●			●	
Maykway Curry Sauce Mix					
Old El Paso Taco Seasoning Mix					
Patak Tandoori Paste					
Patak Tikka Paste					
Rajah All Purpose Seasoning Mix					
Rajah Garlic Powder					
Rajah Kebab Mix					
Rajah Tandoori Masala Mix					
Rani Tandoori Mix			●		
Schwarz Biriani Mix				●	

*US data, may not necessarily apply to UK product ingredients

Wheat	*Soya*	*Flav-En.*	*Colour*	*Pres.*	*Art.Sweet.*
			●		
●	●			z	
			c	●,z	
●	●		●	●	
			●		
				z	
				z	
				z	
			c,●	B	
			●	B	
			c	B	
				B	
●					
				●	
				●	
●	●		●,c		
●	●			●	
		m	●		
	●	m		z	
	●			z	
●		m		B	
		m	c		●
	●		●		
			●		
		m	●,c		
				z	
●	●		c		
			c		
●		m		B	
●		m			
			●		
			c		
			c		
		m			
				s	
●			c		
			c		
			●,c		

Food/Product	Animal	Fish	Insect	Milk	Egg
Schwarz Chop Suey Mix					
Schwarz Sweet & Sour Mix					
Sharwood Tandoori Paste					
Sharwood Sweet & Sour Mix					
Yeo's Malaysian Curry Sauce					
Yeo's Satay Sauce					
Yeo's Sweet & Sour Sauce					
Jacket potato fillings					
Quaker Bacon & Mushroom	●			●	●
Quaker Chicken & Yoghurt	●			●	●
Quaker Ham & Sweetcorn	●			●	●
Quaker Mexican Sauce				●	●
Stratford Mushroom Filler				●	
Stratford Tomato & Mushroom Filler				●	
Stratford Sweeetcorn Filler				●	
Quiches and quiche fillings					
Grove Park Cheese & Onion	●			●	●
Grove Park Vegetarian				●	●
Noodles and noodle soups					
Batchelors Curry-flavour Noodles		●			
Charmela Noodle Soup with spice	●	●			
Cheong-Leen bulk pre-cooked					
Doll Chicken Noodle Soup	●				●
Maggi Malay Noodles		●			●
Nissin Beef Noodle Soup	●				
Nissin Chicken Noodle Soup	●				
Vesta Crispy Noodles					
Preserved vegetables					
Batchelors Dried Garden Peas					
Batchelors Quick-Dried Onions					
Caterers Kitchen Pickled Onions					
Crespa Olives in Brine				●	
Crisp 'n Crunch Pickled Onions					
Dauphine Garlic Puree					
Haywards Pickled Onions				●	
Haywards Sweet Pickled Onions					
Hengstenberg Gherkins (10kg)					
Kauffmann Dill Cucumbers					
Kraft Dill Pickles					
Jumping Fox Dutch Gherkins					

Wheat	Soya	Flav-En.	Colour	Pres.	Art.Sweet.
		m	●		
		m	●		
			c		
		m	●		
		m			
		m			
		m	●		
				n	
				n	
●					
●					
●	●	m,●	c	g,B	●
●	●	m			
●			●		
●	●	m	c,●		
●		●	●	●	
●	●	m	●		
●	●	m	●	●	
●			c		
				s	
				s	
			●	s	
			●	●	
				●,B	
			●	s	
			●	●,s	●
				z	●
					●
			●	●	
					●

Food/Product	*Animal*	*Fish*	*Insect*	*Milk*	*Egg*
Landmark Pickled Onions					
McDougalls Dried Peas					
NVR Dutch Gherkins					
Pandora Sweet Pickled Onions				●	
Suzi-Wan Beansprouts in Brine				●	
Whitworths Quick Dried Onions					
Burger King Pickle Garnish*					
McDonald Dill Pickle*					
Salads and salad dressings					
Batchelors Salad Club Eastern Relish					●
Batchelors Salad Club Mexican Relish					●
Batchelors Salad Club Cucumber Relish					●
Caterers Kitchen Salad Cream				●	●
Eden Vale Vegetable Salad					●
Frank Coopers Salad Cream					●
Kraft Blue Cheese Dressing				●	●
Kraft French-style Dressing					
Kraft Miracle Whip					●
Kraft Onion and Chive Dressing		●			
Kraft Salad Cream					●
Kraft Salad Mayonnaise					●
La Victoria Red Salsa Jalapena					
La Victoria Salsa Picante					
Mattesons Cole Slaw					●
Mattesons "Consumer" Coleslaw					●
Kentucky Fried Chicken Coleslaw					●
Frying fats					
Craigmillar Fat Friar	●				
Craigmillar Tartan	●				
Khanum vegetable ghee					
Narcissus vegetable ghee					
Plough butter ghee					
Burger King French Fries Oil*	●				
McDonald's French Fries Oil*	●				
Wimpy frying oil					
Spreading fats					
Craigmillar Astra	?			●	
Kraft Country	?			●	
Kraft Vitalite	?			●	

Wheat	*Soya*	*Flav-En.*	*Colour*	*Pres.*	*Art.Sweet.*
			●	s	
				s	
					●
			●	s	●
				●	
				z	
				z	
			c	B	
				B	
				B	
			c		●
				z	
			●		
			c		
			●		
			●		
				z	
				z	
			c		●
				●	
				B	
				B	
			●		
			●		
				●	
				g,B	
				B	
				B	
	●		a		
	●		a		
	●		a		

Food/Product	Animal	Fish	Insect	Milk	Egg
Batters and coatings etc					
Birds Golden Raising Powder					
Goldenfry Batter Mix					
Goldensheaf Batter Mix					
Goldensheaf Light Batter Mix					
Goldensheaf Frozen Fish Batter				●	
Goldensheaf Southern Seasoning					
Homepride Southern Seasoning	●				
Crosse & Blackwell Barbecue Burger Seasoning					●
Lion Cooking Crumbs					
Lion Microwave Browning (unseasoned)					
McCormick Fish Seasoning					
McDougalls All Purpose Batter					
Old El Paso Taco seasoning					
Paxo Golden Breadcrumbs					
Schwarz Microwave Browning (seasoned)					
Whitworths Batter Mix					
Burger King Whaler Coating*				●	
Burger King Chicken Coating*				●	
Kentucky Fried Chicken Coating				●	●
McDonald McNuggets Coating*				●	
McDonald Filet-o-Fish Coating*				●	
Wimpy Chicken coating					
Baps, buns and tortillas					
Bejam burger buns	?				●
McDougalls Burger Bap Mix	●				
Mevlit Burger Buns				●	
Tesco Burger Buns	?				
Burger King Buns*	●				
Kara/Kentucky Fried Ch. buns	?				
McDonald Buns*	●				
Taco Bell Tortilla (burrito)*	●				
Taco Bell Tortilla (enchirito)*	●				
Wimpy buns	?			●	
Pizza bases, wafers, muffins, nans, etc.					
Arnaouti wholemeal pitta bread					
Goldenfry pizza base mix	●				
Goldensheaf Pancake Mix				●	●
Goldensheaf Waffle Mix				●	●

* US data, may not necessarily apply to UK product ingredients

Wheat	*Soya*	*Flav-En.*	*Colour*	*Pres.*	*Art.Sweet.*
●			c		
●			c		
●	●		c/a		
●	●				
●	●		c/a		
●	●	m			
●	●			B	
●		m			
●			c		
		m	●		
●		m	●,c	●	
●			c		
			●		
●			●		
		m	●		
●			c		
●					
●		m			
●		m			
●		m			
●			●		
●		m			
●	●				
●					
●					
●					
●					
●	●				h
●				B	
●					
●			c		
●					
●				●	
●					
●					
●	●		c		

Food/Product	*Animal*	*Fish*	*Insect*	*Milk*	*Egg*
Marcantonio ice cream cones					
McCain Master Pizza Base	●			●	
McCain Microwave Master Pizza				●	
McDougalls Pancake Mix	●			●	●
New Vita ice cream cones					
Readi-Bake American Cookies	●			●	●
Sharwood Nan Mix	●			●	
Burger King Onion Rings*				●	●
McDonald's McMuffin*	●			●	
McDonald's Hot Cakes*	?			●	●
Pizza Hut pizza base				●	
Wimpy ice cream wafer					
Wimpy doughnuts					
Burgers					
Baughms Economy Burgers	●				
Birds Eye Original Beefburger	●				
Birds Eye Low Fat Beefburger	●				
Briter Economy Burger	●				
John Butler Economy Burger	●				
Cater Farm Fresh Beefburger	●				
Dietburger (100% vegetable)					
Direct Foods Grain Burger					
Matthews Turkey Burger	●				
Pyke-Biggs 100%	●				
Pyke-Biggs 80%	●				
Westler Hamburger	●				
Westler Burger	●				
Burger King Burger*	●				
McDonald's Burger*	●				
Wimpy Beefburger	●				
Wimpy Beanburger					
Fish and fish products					
Lincolnshire Fishcakes		●			
Burger King Whaler*		●		●	
McDonald Filet-o-Fish*		●			
Wimpy Fish		●			
Chicken and chicken products					
Gotts Cooked Chicken Portions	●				
Hensons Vale Royal Roast Chicken	●				
Matthews Golden Drummers	●				

Wheat	*Soya*	*Flav-En.*	*Colour*	*Pres.*	*Art.Sweet.*
●	●		a,●		●
●				●	
●			a	●,z	
●	●		c	B	
●			c		●
●					
●					
●				B	
●					
●	●				
●				B	
●	●		c		
●	●		c		
●	●	m		s,●	
●		m		s	
●		m		s	
●		m	c	s	
	●			s	
●	●	m	●,c	s	
●	●				
●	●				
●		m		s,●	
				●	
		(●)			
●	●			n	
●	●		●		
		m			
●					
●			●,a		
●					
●					
●					
		m	●		
●				●	

Food/Product	*Animal*	*Fish*	*Insect*	*Milk*	*Egg*
Padleys Chick-n-Quick Fingers	●				
Padleys US-style Drumsticks	●				
Burger King Chicken Specialty*	●			●	
Burger King Chicken Tenders*	●			●	
Kentucky Fried Chicken	●			●	●
McDonald Chicken McNuggets*	●			●	
Wimpy Chicken	●				
Sausages and Saveloys					
Bristol Hot Dog	●			●	
Bowyers Low Fat Sausage	●		●	●	
Direct Foods Vegetarian Sausage					
Farmers Meats Pork Sausage	●				
Freshbake Jumbo Saveloy	●				
Meica Frankfurter	●			●	
Plumtree Cumberland Sausage	●				
Plumtree Pork Sausage	●				
Tasty Bake Quality Saveloy	●				
Westlers Hot Dogs	●			●	
Burger King Sausage*	●				
McDonald Sausage*	●				
Wimpy Bender	●				
Savoury pies, pasties and sausage rolls					
Gillards Beef & Onion Pie	●			●	●
Gillards Chicken & Mushroom Pie	●			●	●
Gillards Cornish Pasty	●			●	●
Gillards Steak & Kidney Pie	●			●	
Jus-Rol Cornish Pasty	●			●	
Jus-Rol Lincolnshire Sausage Roll	●				
Jus-Rol Sausage Roll	●				
Peters Chicken & Mushroom Pie	●			●	
Peters Cornish Pasty	●			●	
Peters Pork Pie	●			●	
Peters Sausage Roll	●			●	
Peters Steak & Kidney Pie	●			●	
Waldens Sausage Roll	●			●	
Waldens Steak & Kidney Pie	●				
Waldens Traditional Cornish Pasty	●			●	
Other meat products					
Danish Bacon Nuggets	●				
Danish Bacon Fingers	●				

Wheat	Soya	Flav-En.	Colour	Pres.	Art.Sweet.
●	●				
●					
●		m			
●		m			
●		m			
●		m		B	
●		m			
	●			●,n	
●			●	s,●	
●	●		●		
●	●	m		s,●	
	●	m	c	s	
				n,●	
●				s,●	
●	●	m	c	s,●	
●	●	m	●		
		m	c	n,●	
		m			
		m		B	
				n,●	
●	●	m	●		
●	●				
●	●	m			
●	●	m	●		
●		m			
●	●	m			
●	●	m	c		
●		m			
●		m			
●		m		●,n	
●		m			
●		m			
●			●,a	B,s,●	
●	●	m	●,a	B	
●			●,a	B	
●	●			●,n	
●	●	m		●,n	

Food/Product	*Animal*	*Fish*	*Insect*	*Milk*	*Egg*
Dinos Cold Honey Roast Ham	●			●	
Epicure Cold Ham	●				
Express Cold Chicken Roll	●				
Express Cold Cured Chicken Roll	●			●	
Mattesons Cold Pork Shoulder	●			●	
Mattesons Huntingdon Ham	●				
Mattesons Cold Turkey Breast	●				
Matthews Cheese Hamwich	●			●	
Peters Cold Pork Shoulder	●			●	
Sun Valley Cold Turkey Breast	●			●	
Transfoods Cold Beef	●			●	
Burger King Ham*	●				
Burger King Bacon*	●				
McDonald Bacon*	●				
Wimpy Bacon	●				
Cheese					
Adams Catering Processed Cheese				●	
Kraft Burger Cheese Slices				●	
Kraft Original Cheese Slices				●	
St Ivel Grated Cheddar				●	
St Ivel Cheddaplus				●	
St Ivel Mozzaplus				●	
Burger King Cheese*				●	
McDonald Cheese*				●	
Wimpy Cheese				●	
Chips, fries and potato products					
Jus-Rol Potato Croquettes					●
McCain Hash Browns					
Burger King French Fries*					
Burger King Hash Browns*					
McDonald French Fries*					
McDonald Hash Browns*	●				
Pizzas and pizza toppings					
McCain Master Pizza	●			●	
McCain Microwave Master Pizza				●	
Tender Land Pizza Sauce					
Pizza Hut (with meat topping)	●			●	
Pizza Hut (ham/pepperoni topping)	●			●	
Pizza Hut (with anchovies)		●		●	
Pizza Hut (non-meat)				●	

Wheat	*Soya*	*Flav-En.*	*Colour*	*Pres.*	*Art.Sweet.*
		m		n,●	
		m		n	
●	●				
				●,n	
	●	m		n	
		m		n	
			●		
●		m		●,n	
●		m	a	●,n	
		m			
			●		
				n	
				n,B	
				n	
				n,●	
			●		
			●	●	
			●	●	
			●		
			●	●	
				●	
	●		a,●		
				●	
			●	●	
●			a		
		m			
				B	
				B	
●					
●				●	
●			a,●	●,z	
				●	
●		m		B	
●		m		B,n	
●				B	
●				B	

Food/Product	Animal	Fish	Insect	Milk	Egg
Chinese-style dishes					
Bejam Spare Ribs in BBQ Sauce	●	?			
Bejam Ribs in Chinese-style Sauce	●				
Daloon Pancake Rolls	●			●	●
La Choy Fried Rice					
La Choy Chop Suey Vegetables					
La Choy Shrimp Chow Mein		●			
Mr Chang Beef Chop Suey	●				
Mr Chang Chicken Chow Mein	●				
Mr Chang Chicken Curry	●				
Mr Chang Special Fried Rice	●				●
Pan Chop Suey Rolls	●			●	●
Suzi Wan Stir-fry Rice	●				
Unger King Ribs Chinese	●				
Unger King Ribs BBQ	●				
Mexican-style dishes					
Old El Paso Chili con Carne	●				
Old El Paso Beef Taco Filling	●				
Vesta Tostadas	●				
Vesta Tacos	●				
Taco Bell Beans*	●				
Taco Bell Flour Tortilla*	●				
Taco Bell Flour Tortilla for Enchirito*	●				
Greek-style dishes					
(various brands) Humus					
(various brands) Taramasalata		●			
Desserts					
Frisiana Cornish Ice Cream Mix	?			●	
Frisiana Ice Cream Powder	?			●	
Luna Soft Ice Cream	?			●	
Readi-Bake American Cookies	●			●	●
Scottish Dairy Ice Cream	?			●	
Vitari Soft Fruit Whip					
Wispy Soft-serve Dessert				●	
Baskin Robbins Ice Creams	?			●	
Burger King Apple Pie*				●	
Kentucky Fried Chicken Apple Pie (cold)					
Kentucky Fried Chicken Apple Pie (hot)					
McDonald Apple Pie*	●			●	

Wheat	*Soya*	*Flav-En.*	*Colour*	*Pres.*	*Art.Sweet.*
●	●		c		
●	●	m	●,c	●	
●	●				
		m	●		
		m			
		m			
	●	m			
	●	m			
●		m			
	●	m			
	●	m			
		m		●	
●		m	●,c		●
●		m	●		
●		m		n	
		m		n	
●		m		●,s,B	
●		m	c	●,s,B	
●					
●			c		
				●/z	
			c/a	●/z	
			c/a		
●					
			●,a		
●			●		
●	●		●		
●				●,s	
●					
●				B,g	

Food/Product	*Animal*	*Fish*	*Insect*	*Milk*	*Egg*
McDonald Birthday Cakes*	?			●	●
Wimpy Apple Pie	?				
Wimpy Ice Creams	?			●	
Wimpy Mince and Apple Pie	?				
Beverages					
Caterers Kitchen Whole Orange Drink					
Frisiana Triple Milk Shake Powder				●	
McDougall's Shake Powders and Syrups					
Wander Thick Milkshake Mix					
Coke					
Diet Coke					
Fanta					
Pepsi					
Diet Pepsi					
7-Up*					
Burger King Milk Shakes*	?			●	
McDonald Milk Shakes*				●	
McDonald Orange Drink*					
McDonald Root Beer*					
Wimpy Milk Shakes				●	

*US data, may not necessarily apply to UK product ingredients

Appendix 3 **Your points of contact**

In this section we indicate the people you might turn to when you want to do something about fast foods. We list the major companies' UK addresses and where appropriate their overseas headquarters. We list the government departments responsible for regulating our food and changing the law. And we list the organisations that can offer support: the local authority staff who monitor the food companies' activities, the health service staff who can give advice on getting what we need for our health, and the voluntary bodies and consumer groups who can help campaign for a better deal for us, the fast food eaters.

Wheat	Soya	Flav-En.	Colour	Pres.	Art.Sweet.
●			a		
●					
	●		●,a	●	
●			●		
			c	z,s	●
			c		
			c		
			●		
			●	z	●
			c	z	
			●		
			●	z	●
				z	
			a,c	z	
			c	z	
			c	z	
			●	z	
			c	z,s	

The Companies:

Allied-Lyons
Allied House
156 St John Street
London EC1P 1AR
Tel: 01-253 9911

Associated Fisheries
16 Queen Anne's Gate
London SW1H 9AQ
Tel: 01-222 0404

Baskin Robbins
79 Muswell Hill
London N10 3PH
Tel: 01-444 4141

Burger King (UK)
20 Kew Road
Richmond
Surrey
Tel: 01-940 6046

Casey Jones/Travellers Fare
British Rail Catering
Tournament House
Paddington Station
London W2 1HQ
Tel: 01-723 7000

Deep Pan Pizza Co
Garfunkels
57 Duke Street
London W1
Tel: 01-499 5000

Grand Metropolitan
11/12 Hanover Square
London W1A 1DP
Tel: 01-629 7488

Kentucky Fried Chicken
Wicat House
403 London Road
Camberley
Surrey GU15 3HL
Tel: 0276-686151

Little Chef/Happy Eater/etc
Trusthouse Forte
12 Sherwood Street
London W1
Tel: 01-437 7788

McDonald's Hamburgers
11/59 High Road
Finchley
London N2 8AW
Tel: 01-883 6400

Pizza Hut/Taco Bell
Eurafme House
2 Woodgrange Avenue
Kenton
Middlesex HA3 0XD
Tel: 01-907 4388

Pizza Express
29 Wardour Street
London W1V 3HB
Tel: 01-437 7215

Pizzaland
65 Staines Road
Hounslow
Middlesex TW3 3HW
Tel: 01-570 2323

Rank Hovis McDougall
RHM Centre
P O Box 178
Alma Road
Windsor
Berkshire SL4 3ST
Tel: Windsor 57123

Rowntree Mackintosh
York YO1 1XY
Tel: 0904-53071

Spud-U-Like
34/38 Standard Road
London NW10 6EU
Tel: 01-965 0182

Unilever
Unilever House
Blackfriars
London EC4P 4BQ
Tel: 01-822 5252

United Biscuits
Grant House
Syon Lane
Isleworth
Middlesex TW7 5NN
Tel: 01-560 3131

Wimpy
10 Windmill Road
London W4 1SD
Tel: 01-994 6454

The government departments

Your MP*
House of Commons
Westminster
London SW1
Tel: 01-219 3000

*to find our who your MP is, phone the House of Commons Library
Tel: 01-219 4272

Ministry of Agriculture, Fisheries and Food
Whitehall Place
London SW1A 2HH
Tel: 01-233 3000

Department of the Environment
2 Marsham Street
London SW1P 3EB
Tel: 01-212 3434

Department of Health
Alexander Fleming House
Elephant and Castle
London SE1 6BY
Tel: 01-407 5522

Department of Trade and Industry
1 Victoria Street
London SW1H 0ET
Tel: 01-215 7877

Local authorities

Local authorities are responsible for, among many other things, planning permission, environmental health and trading standards. If you have complaints about the activities or proposed activities of a fast food outlet, you might start by contacting these departments in your local town hall. We cannot list all the departments and their addresses for the country. But we can give the Town Hall phone numbers, to get you going:

Avon 0272-290777
Barking & Dagenham 01-592 4500
Barnet 01-202 8282
Barnsley 0226-203232
Bedfordshire 0234-63222
Berkshire 0734-875444
Bexley 01-303 7777
Birmingham 021-235 2037
Bolton 00204-22311
Borders 08352-53301
Brent 01-903 1400
Bromley 01-464 3333
Buckinghamshire 0296-5000
Bury 061-764 6000
Cambridgeshire 0223-317111
Camden 01-278 4444
Central 0786-73111
Cheshire 0244-602424
City of London Corpn 01-606 3030
Cleveland 0642-248155
Clwyd 0352-2121
Cornwall 08727-4282
Coventry 00203-25555
Croydon 01-686 4433
Cumbria 0228-23456
Derbyshire 0629-3411
Devon 0392-77977
Doncaster 0302-734444
Dorset 0305-63131
Dudley 0384-55433
Dumfries & Galloway 0387-3141
Durham 0385-64411
Dyfed 0267-233333
Ealing 01-579 2424
East Sussex 0273-475400
Enfield 01-366 6565
Essex 0245-267222
Fife 0592-754411
Gateshead 0632-771011
Gloucestershire 0452-21444
Grampian 0224-682222
Greenwich 01-854 8888
States of Guernsey 0481-27412
Gwent 06333-67711
Gwynedd 0286-4121
Hackney 01-986 3123

Hammersmith & Fulham 01-748 3020
Hampshire 0962-54411
Haringey 01-888 3000
Harrow 01-863 5611
Havering 01-0708-46040
Hereford & Worcester 0905-353366
Hertfordshire 0992-54242
Highland 0463-234121
Hillingdon 0895-50111
Hounslow 01-570 7728
Humberside 0482-867131
Isle of Man 0624-26262
Isle of White 098352-4031
Islington 01-226 1234
States of Jersey 0534-27286
Kensington & Chelsea 01-937 5464
Kent 0622-671411
Kingston upon Thames 01-546 2121
Knowsley 051-548 6555
Lambeth 01-274 7722
Lancashire 0772-54868
Leicestershire 0533-871313
Lewisham 01-690 4343
Lincolnshire 0522-29931
Liverpool 051-227 3911
Lothian 031-229 9292
Manchester 061-236 3377
Merton 01-946 8070
Mid Glamorgan 0222-28033
Newcastle upon Tyne 0632-328520
Newham 01-472 1430
Norfolk 0603-611122
Northamptonshire 0604-34833
Northumberland 0670-514343
Northern Ireland 0232-647151
North Tyneside 0632-575544
North Yorkshire 0609-3123
Nottinghamshire 0602-823823
Oldham 061-624 0505
Orkney Islands 0856-3535
Oxfordshire 0865-722422
Powys 0597-3711
Redbridge 01-478 3020
Richmond upon Thames 01-891 1411
Rochdale 0706-47474
Rotherham 0709-2121
St Helens 0744-24061
Sandwell 021-569 2200
Sefton 051-992 4040
Sheffield 0742-26444
Shetland Islands 0595-3535
Shropshire 0743-222100
Solihull 021-705 6789
Somerset 0823-73451
South Glamorgan 0222-499022
South Tyneside 0632-554321
Southwark 01-703 6311
Staffordshire 0785-3121
Stockport 061-480 4949
Strathclyde 041-204 2900
Suffolk 0473-55801
Sunderland 0783-76161
Surrey 01-546 1050
Sutton 01-661 5000
Tameside 061-330 8355
Tayside 0382-23281
Tower Hamlets 01-980 4831
Trafford 061-872 2101
Walsall 0922-21244
Waltham Forest 01-527 544
Wandsworth 01-871 6060
Warwickshire 0926-493431
Western Isles 0851-3773
West Glamorgan 0792-471111
Westminster 01-828 8070
West Sussex 0243-777100
Wigan 0942-44991
Wiltshire 02214-3641
Wirral 051-638 7070
Wolverhampton 0902-27811

Advice from local health workers

If you need more advice on nutrition or you want to arrange a meeting with a speaker, then contact your local health authority. Members of their Dietetics, Health Education and Community Dental Health Departments should be able to help you.

Health Authority departments are found through your local hospital or through your local Community Health Council – these should be listed in your phone directory. Otherwise, here are the Regional Health Authorities who should be able to give you the number you want.

East Anglia (for Cambridgeshire, Norfolk, Suffolk) 0223-61212

Mersey (for Cheshire, Merseyside) 051-236 8464

Northern (for Cleveland, Cumbria, Durham, Northumberland, Newcastle, North Tyneside, Gateshead, South Tyneside, Sunderland) 0632-654188

N Ireland Central Services 0232-224431

North Western (for Lancashire, Wigan, Bolton, Bury, Rochdale, Salford, Manchester, Oldham, Trafford, Stockport, Tameside) 061-236 9465

Oxford (for Berkshire, Buckinghamshire, Northamptonshire, Oxfordshire) 0865-64861

Scottish Common Services 031-552 6255

South Western (for Avon, Cornwall, Devon, Somerset, Gloucestershire) 0272-423271

Thames, North East (for Essex, City, Camden, Barking, Enfield, Hackney, Haringey, Havering, Islington, Newham, Redbridge, Tower Hamlets, Waltham Forest) 01-262 8011

Thames, North West (for Bedfordshire, Hertfordshire, Barnet, Brent, Ealing, Hammersmith and Fulham, Harrow, Hillingdon, Hounslow, Kensington and Chelsea, Westminster) 01-262 8011

Thames, South East (for East Sussex, Kent, Bexley, Greenwich, Bromley, Lambeth, Lewisham, Southwark) 0424-222555

Thames, South West (for Surrey, West Sussex, Croydon, Kingson upon Thames, Merton, Richmond upon Thames, Sutton, Wandsworth) 01-262 8011

Trent (for Derbyshire, Lincolnshire, Leicestershire, Nottinghamshire, Barnsley, Doncaster, Sheffield, Rotherham) 0742-306511

Wessex (for Dorset, Hampshire, Wiltshire, Isle of Wight) 0962-63511

West Midlands (for Hereford and Worcester, Shropshire, Staffordshire, Warwickshire, Walsall, Wolverhampton, Dudley, Sandwell, Birmingham, Coventry, Solihull) 021-454 4828

Yorkshire (for Humberside, North Yorkshire, Bradford, Leeds, Calderdale, Kirklees, Wakefield) 0423-65061

Welsh Health Services 0222-499921

Consumer organisations

Write to these bodies and ask them what their current activities are with respect to food issues and campaigns. Ask for their publication lists and recent copies of their magazines and reports.

Bureau Européen des Unions de Consommateurs
29 Rue Royale Bte 3
1000 Brussels
Belgium
Tel: 010-32-2 218 3093

Centre for Science in the Public Interest
1501 16th Street NW
Washington
DC 20036
Tel: 010-1-202 332 9110

Consumers' Association
14 Buckingham Street
London WC2N 6DS
Tel: 01-839 1222

Consumers in the European Community Group
24 Tufton Street
London SW1P 3RB
Tel: 01-222 2662

European Consumers Consultative Committee
200 Rue de la Loi
B-1040 Brussels
Belgium

International Organisation of Consumer Unions
9 Emmastraat
2595 EG
The Hague
Netherlands
Tel: 010-31-70 476331

Institute of Trading Standards Administration
Metropolitan House
37 Victoria Avenue
Southend-on-Sea
SS2 6DA
Tel: 0702-338313